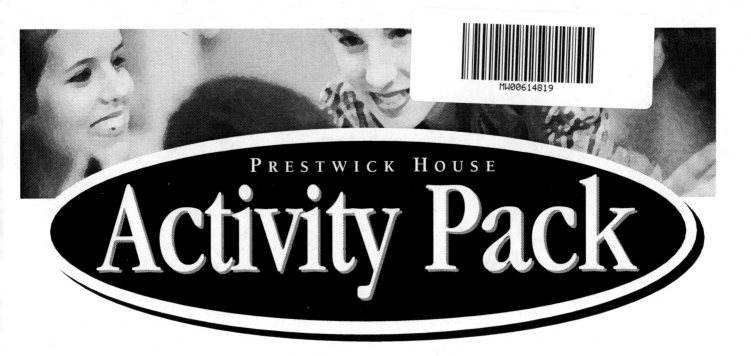

PRESTWICK HOUSE

Activity Pack

MACBETH

BY WILLIAM SHAKESPEARE

Copyright © 2003 by Prestwick House, Inc., P.O. Box 658, Clayton, DE 19938. 1-800-932-4593. www.prestwickhouse.com Permission to use this unit for classroom use is extended to purchaser for his or her personal use. This material, in whole or part, may not be copied for resale.

ISBN-10   1-58049-623-7
ISBN-13 978-1-58049-623-0

Reorder No. 200161

Macbeth

Table of Contents

Appendix

MACBETH

Activity Pack
Teacher's Edition

Pre-reading

Research

Objective: Researching the author

Activity

Research the life of William Shakespeare and write a short biography. Explain why most scholars consider him to be the greatest playwright who ever wrote in English. Include any significant facts about Shakespeare's inspiration for *Macbeth*. Write at least four paragraphs.

MACBETH

Activity Pack
Student Edition

Pre-reading

Research

Objective: Researching the author

Activity

Research the life of William Shakespeare and write a short biography. Explain why most scholars consider him to be the greatest playwright who ever wrote in English. Include any significant facts about Shakespeare's inspiration for *Macbeth*. Write at least four paragraphs.

Pre-reading

Setting
History

Objective: Researching the historical setting of the play

Activity

Beyond the witches and the ghosts, the political events that occur in *Macbeth* are realistic for the time and the place in which the play is set. In medieval Scotland, kings were overthrown on a regular basis and often through violent means.

Use the library, the Internet, or both to research the setting of *Macbeth*. Begin by searching for the early history of Scotland (between the years 850 – 1100). *Macbeth* and Shakespeare websites will be helpful, as will the history of specific places in the setting. Use the information that you find to fill out the **Setting Chart** on the next page.

Some of the topics on the **Setting Chart** are more applicable to the timeframe than the location of *Macbeth*, such as "Historical Events" or "Inventions." These apply to the entire world during the target period of your research.

Pre-reading

Setting
History

Objective: Researching the historical setting of the play

Activity

Beyond the witches and the ghosts, the political events that occur in *Macbeth* are realistic for the time and the place in which the play is set. In medieval Scotland, kings were overthrown on a regular basis and often through violent means.

Use the library, the Internet, or both to research the setting of *Macbeth*. Begin by searching for the early history of Scotland (between the years 850 – 1100). *Macbeth* and Shakespeare websites will be helpful, as will the history of specific places in the setting. Use the information that you find to fill out the **Setting Chart** on the next page.

Some of the topics on the **Setting Chart** are more applicable to the timeframe than the location of *Macbeth*, such as "Historical Events" or "Inventions." These apply to the entire world during the target period of your research.

Setting Chart: Scotland, 850 – 1100 C.E.

Topic	Description

Area
 	
    Location
 	
    Population
 	
    Bordering Nations
 	
    Geographic Description
	Scotland

Government
 	
    Political System
 	
    Succession of Rulers
 	
    Economic System
 	
    Major Religions	

World Facts
 	
    Significant Names
 	
    Historical Events
 	
    Inventions
 	
    Literature	

Approximate period in which *Macbeth* takes place	

Note to teacher: For an extended activity, students could consolidate information acquired and write a three-page research paper.

Setting Chart: Scotland, 850 – 1100 C.E.

Topic	Description
Area Location Population Bordering Nations Geographic Description	Scotland
Government Political System Succession of Rulers Economic System Major Religions	
World Facts Significant Names Historical Events Inventions Literature	
Approximate period in which *Macbeth* takes place	

Pre-reading

Word Game

Objective: Finding words within words

Activity

Many of the names in *Macbeth* are uncommon in our culture; however, they all contain many hidden words. Your job is to find these hidden words.

Example: The word *Macbeth* contains the letters to spell many other words: ace, act, beach, cab, came, each, eat, hat, math, tame, etc.

See how many words you can make from each word on the list below. Use each letter only as many times as it appears in each word. The words you find must have at least three letters.

Donalbain –

Banquo –

Lennox –

Menteith –

Angus –

Caithness –

Fleance –

Siward –

Seyton –

Dunsinane –

Pre-reading

Word Game

Objective: Finding words within words

Activity

Many of the names in *Macbeth* are uncommon in our culture; however, they all contain many hidden words. Your job is to find these hidden words.

Example: The word *Macbeth* contains the letters to spell many other words: ace, act, beach, cab, came, each, eat, hat, math, tame, etc.

See how many words you can make from each word on the list below. Use each letter only as many times as it appears in each word. The words you find must have at least three letters.

Donalbain –

Banquo –

Lennox –

Menteith –

Angus –

Caithness –

Fleance –

Siward –

Seyton –

Dunsinane –

Pre-reading

Research

Objective: Comparing the author's contemporaries

Activity

Research and make notations on the list of people on the **Shakespeare's Contemporaries Chart**. These are notable people from Shakespeare's time period.

Complete the chart for each of the names. Record the respective field for the contemporary, his country of origin, year of birth and death, and any historical accomplishments. The first example has been completed for you.

SHAKESPEARE'S CONTEMPORARIES CHART

Person	Origin	Field	Accomplishment
John Donne (1572-1631)	England	Literature	Poet "Songs & Sonnets"
John Milton (1608-1674)	England	Literature	Poet "Paradise Lost"
Ambroise Pare (1510-1590)	France	Science	Invented early prosthetics
Konrad Gesner (1516-1565)	Switzerland	Science	Invented graphite pencil
Zacharius Jansen (circa 1500-1590)	Netherlands	Science	Invented compound microscope
Johann Sebastian Bach (1685-1750)	Germany	Music	Composer
Antonio Vivaldi (1675-1741)	Italy	Music	Composer
Rene Descartes (1596-1650)	France	Philosophy	Philosopher; famous for "I think, therefore I am"
Benedict Spinoza (1632-1677)	Netherlands	Philosophy	Theories of deductive reasoning; famous for "knowledge is power"

Pre-reading

Research

Objective: Comparing the author's contemporaries

Activity

Research and make notations on the list of people on the **Shakespeare's Contemporaries Chart**. These are notable people from Shakespeare's time period.

Complete the chart for each of the names. Record the respective field for the contemporary, his country of origin, year of birth and death, and any historical accomplishments. The first example has been completed for you.

SHAKESPEARE'S CONTEMPORARIES CHART

Person	Origin	Field	Accomplishment
John Donne (1572-1631)	England	Literature	Poet "Songs & Sonnets"
John Milton (1608-1674)			
Ambroise Pare (1510-1590)			
Konrad Gesner (1516-1565)			
Zacharius Jansen (circa 1500-1590)			
Johann Sebastian Bach (1685-1750)			
Antonio Vivaldi (1675-1741)			
Rene Descartes (1596-1650)			
Benedict Spinoza (1632-1677)			

Pre-reading

Advertising

Objective: Creating a playbill

Activity

Shakespeare existed long before the present age of mass communication. Playwrights in Shakespeare's era had to rely on word-of-mouth and simple playbills, or flyers, to advertise their productions. Limited printing technology meant that playbills were mostly text and had only one—if any—simple drawing. The playbill usually included the name of the production, the playwright, the time and location of the performance, the names of the actors and characters, and a brief description of the play.

Divide the class into small groups. Each group should design a modern playbill for *Macbeth*. The playbill should be no larger than one page, but it should contain enough information to convince someone to see *Macbeth*.

Use any available resources to make the playbills. They can be completely hand drawn, computer generated, or any combination of the two. Remember, the text on the playbill should be eye-catching but readable. Any drawings should be relevant to the play, but dramatic enough to spark someone's interest.

Complete one flyer per group.

Pre-reading

Advertising

Objective: Creating a playbill

Activity

Shakespeare existed long before the present age of mass communication. Playwrights in Shakespeare's era had to rely on word-of-mouth and simple playbills, or flyers, to advertise their productions. Limited printing technology meant that playbills were mostly text and had only one—if any—simple drawing. The playbill usually included the name of the production, the playwright, the time and location of the performance, the names of the actors and characters, and a brief description of the play.

Each group should design a modern playbill for *Macbeth*.
The playbill should be no larger than one page, but it should contain enough information to convince someone to see *Macbeth*.

Use any available resources to make the playbills. They can be completely hand drawn, computer generated, or any combination of the two. Remember, the text on the playbill should be eye-catching but readable. Any drawings should be relevant to the play, but dramatic enough to spark someone's interest.

Complete one flyer per group.

Act I

Characterization

Objective: Recognizing character traits

Activity

Reading a play like *Macbeth* is exciting, but unfortunately one element is missing: physical descriptions of the characters. Drama is designed to be watched—not read. Viewers may see for themselves the physical details of characters in a play, so the printed form need not contain descriptions common to standard literature.

When reading drama, one must pay close attention in order to mentally complete the character details. Much of the detail is secondary; we read what one character says or thinks about another character. We also gain character information by observing the actions of characters.

Complete the **Character Chart** to reveal your assessment of the characters in the first Act. When you are finished with the chart, review the characters that you designated as "major characters." Select the two most similar characters and write one paragraph comparing them. Next, select the two least similar characters and write another paragraph, this time contrasting them.

You may not yet have the information to fill in some of the blocks. When this occurs, write "NI" in the appropriate space.

Act I

Characterization

Objective: Recognizing character traits

Activity

Reading a play like *Macbeth* is exciting, but unfortunately one element is missing: physical descriptions of the characters. Drama is designed to be watched—not read. Viewers may see for themselves the physical details of characters in a play, so the printed form need not contain descriptions common to standard literature.

When reading drama, one must pay close attention in order to mentally complete the character details. Much of the detail is secondary; we read what one character says or thinks about another character. We also gain character information by observing the actions of characters.

Complete the **Character Chart** to reveal your assessment of the characters in the first Act. When you are finished with the chart, review the characters that you designated as "major characters." Select the two most similar characters and write one paragraph comparing them. Next, select the two least similar characters and write another paragraph, this time contrasting them.

You may not yet have the information to fill in some of the blocks. When this occurs, write "NI" in the appropriate space.

CHARACTER CHART

Character	Trade	Moral Alignment – Personality Traits	Concerns, Goals	Major Character?
Witches	*Withered, wild. Old age. Witches.*	*Evil. ("Fair is foul and foul is fair"); cryptic speakers; mischievous.*	*Spreading evil.*	*Yes*
Duncan	*King of Scotland*	*Good. social; generous with praise; well liked; loyal to friends.*	*Stopping the revolt; executing Cawdor; rewarding his subjects.*	*Yes*
Malcolm	*Son of King; Prince of Cumberland*	*Good. Loyal to father. Respectful to subordinates.*	*Becoming King.*	*Yes*
Sergeant	*Soldier*	*Good. Hearty soldier. Loyal to King.*	*Getting his wounds treated.*	*No*
Ross	*Nobleman, messenger*	*Good. Loyal to King.*	*NI*	*NI*
Lennox	*Nobleman*	*NI.*	*NI*	*NI*
Macbeth	*Scottish General*	*Evil. Valiant soldier and general. First loyal, then greedy.*	*The prophecy; becoming King; bringing himself to kill Duncan.*	*Yes*
Banquo	*Scottish General*	*Good. Reassuring friend to Macbeth; observant.*	*NI*	*Yes*
Angus	*Nobleman, messenger*	*Loyal to King.*	*NI*	*No*
Lady Macbeth	*Wife of Macbeth*	*Evil. Domineering; nagging; ambitious.*	*Help husband take over the throne.*	*Yes*

CHARACTER CHART

Character	Trade	Moral Alignment – Personality Traits	Concerns, Goals	Major Character?
Witches				
Duncan				
Malcolm				
Sergeant				
Ross				
Lennox				
Macbeth				
Banquo				
Angus				
Lady Macbeth				

Act II

Outlining

Objective: Writing an outline

Activity

Imagine that you are a Hollywood screenwriter who must convert the theatrical *Macbeth* to movie format. Each scene will be filmed separately, and the actors and crew will need help remembering the details of each scene. Outline each act by scenes and assign a title to each one. Give a brief description of the events in each scene. The title should reflect the content of the respective act or scene.

Note to teacher: These pages should be retained and completed as students progress through the play.

When you finish the outline, think of three alternate titles for *Macbeth*: *the Movie*.

Example:

I.   Act I: Macbeth acquires a new fate
    A. Scene I: The witches' first meeting
        1. Three witches meet in a deserted place
        2. Witches plan a future meeting with Macbeth
    B. Scene II: Duncan speaks with the sergeant
        1. Sergeant informs King of victory over Norwegians
        2. Sergeant describes Macbeth as heroic
    C. Scene III: Macbeth encounters the witches
        1. Witches give Macbeth a prophecy
        2.   Banquo reassures Macbeth
        3. Ross and Angus confirm the prophecy
    D. Scene IV: Macbeth meets with Duncan
        1.   Duncan praises Macbeth
        2.   Macbeth reveals his "deep desires"
    E. Scene V: Lady Macbeth plots the murder of Duncan
        1.   Lady Macbeth receives letter from Macbeth
        2.   Duncan approaches castle Macbeth
        3.   Lady Macbeth tells Macbeth to behave normally around Duncan
    F. Scene VI: Duncan arrives at Macbeth's castle
        1.   Lady Macbeth welcomes Duncan
        2.   Duncan asks for Macbeth
    G. Scene VII: Lady Macbeth reveals details of the murder
        1.   Macbeth is uncertain about the assassination
        2.   Lady Macbeth convinces Macbeth to proceed with murder

Act II

Outlining

Objective: Writing an outline

Activity

Imagine that you are a Hollywood screenwriter who must convert the theatrical *Macbeth* to movie format. Each scene will be filmed separately, and the actors and crew will need help remembering the details of each scene. Outline each act by scenes and assign a title to each one. Give a brief description of the events in each scene. The title should reflect the content of the respective act or scene.

When you finish the outline, think of three alternate titles for *Macbeth: the Movie*.

Example:

I.   Act I: Macbeth acquires a new fate
    A. Scene I: The witches' first meeting
            1. Three witches meet in a deserted place
            2. Witches plan a future meeting with Macbeth
    B. Scene II: Duncan speaks with the sergeant
            1. Sergeant informs King of victory over Norwegians
            2. Sergeant describes Macbeth as heroic
    C. Scene III: Macbeth encounters the witches
            1. Witches give Macbeth a prophecy
            2. Banquo reassures Macbeth
            3. Ross and Angus confirm the prophecy
    D. Scene IV: Macbeth meets with Duncan
            1. Duncan praises Macbeth
            2. Macbeth reveals his "deep desires"
    E. Scene V: Lady Macbeth plots the murder of Duncan
            1. Lady Macbeth receives letter from Macbeth
            2. Duncan approaches castle Macbeth
            3. Lady Macbeth tells Macbeth to behave normally around Duncan
    F. Scene VI: Duncan arrives at Macbeth's castle
            1. Lady Macbeth welcomes Duncan
            2. Duncan asks for Macbeth
    G. Scene VII: Lady Macbeth reveals details of the murder
            1. Macbeth is uncertain about the assassination
            2. Lady Macbeth convinces Macbeth to proceed with murder

II.   Act II:

Continue the outline as you complete each Act.

II.   Act II:

Continue the outline as you complete each Act.

Act II

Simile

Objective: Recognizing a simile

Activity

Shakespeare's drama is full of simile; however, we might not easily recognize the objects that he uses for comparison due to the evolution of language. In Act III, scene four, Macbeth describes himself as "broad and general as the casing air." (Pg. 42) Today, we would probably use the equivalent simile, "free as the wind."

In Acts I and II, identify six instances of simile. List them on the **Simile Chart** that follows and then interpret them. For each interpretation, try to include a modern simile that carries the same message as the original.

The first example has been completed for you.

Note to teacher: These are only examples. There are numerous others.

Act II

Simile

Objective: Recognizing a simile

Activity

Shakespeare's drama is full of simile; however, we might not easily recognize the objects that he uses for comparison due to the evolution of language. In Act III, scene four, Macbeth describes himself as "broad and general as the casing air." (Pg. 42) Today, we would probably use the equivalent simile, "free as the wind."

In Acts I and II, identify six instances of simile. List them on the **Simile Chart** that follows and then interpret them. For each interpretation, try to include a modern simile that carries the same message as the original.

The first example has been completed for you.

Simile Chart

Original Simile	Act, Scene Character	Interpretation
"Doubtful it stood; / As two spent swimmers, that do cling together / And choke their art."	Act I, Scene 2 Sergeant	The Sergeant compares the two sides of the battle to two tired swimmers who cling to each other and drown as a result.
"Macbeth . . . Like valour's minion carved out his passage"	Act I, Scene 2 Sergeant	Macbeth fought like a slave to valor (bravery)
"[Macbeth and Banquo are dismayed] As sparrows eagles, or the hare to lion.	Act I, Scene 2 Sergeant	The enemy attack scares Macbeth and Banquo as much as a sparrow would scare an eagle or a hare would scare a lion
"they [Macbeth and Banquo] were / As cannons overcharged with double cracks"	Act I, Scene 2 Sergeant	The generals were as effective as cannons double-loaded with powder
"I will drain him dry as hay"	Act I, Scene 3 First Witch	The witch will frighten the sailor so much that his life will drain from him, until he is as "dry as hay"
"when in swinish sleep / Their drenched natures lie as in a death"	Act I, Scene 7 Macbeth	The guards will be in a deep sleep, like death, because they are intoxicated
"And his [Duncan's] gash'd stabs look'd like a breach in nature / For ruin's wasteful entrance"	Act II, Scene 3 Macbeth	Macbeth compares Duncan's wound to a hole into which destruction enters

Simile Chart

Original Simile	Act, Scene Character	Interpretation
"Doubtful it stood; / As two spent swimmers, that do cling together / And choke their art."	Act I, Scene 2 Sergeant	The Sergeant compares the two sides of the battle to two tired swimmers who cling to each other and drown as a result.

Act II

Newspaper Reporting

Objective: Writing a news story about the play

Activity

News reporters must be keen observers of the events that they cover, especially when the information they distribute has the potential to influence the general public. During war and other large-scale events, for example, people on the home front await reports from the front lines in order to evaluate the situation for themselves. The information must be carefully reviewed and free of personal opinion or exaggeration because it has the potential to cast an entire nation into panic. False or improper information may also cause harm to the public; it can sway political opinions, create enemies with other nations, or cause instability in the government.

You are a modern reporter who has been transported through time to medieval Scotland in order to compile a story on the murder of Duncan. Observe what you can from the characters involved with the event and record the answers to the fundamental questions of a reporter: who, what, when, where, how, and why? Once you've acquired those answers, write an article covering the event. Include a headline and be sure to keep the article factual and free of your own opinion.

Your first paragraph should be a condensed version of the event. The remainder of the article should contain any other significant information surrounding the murder; remember, in journalism, the *unanswered* questions are just as important as the answered questions.

Below is an example as to how your article might begin:

DUNCAN ASSASSINATED!

> INVERNESS. The calm after the battle was shattered today when Duncan, King of Scotland, was found murdered in the castle of General Macbeth. Also killed were two guards suspected of conducting the assassination. "O horror, horror, horror!" cried the shaken nobleman Macduff upon discovering the murdered Duncan.

Note to teacher: As a follow up activity, students could write the article in Elizabethan English.

Act II

Newspaper Reporting

Objective: Writing a news story about the play

Activity

News reporters must be keen observers of the events that they cover, especially when the information they distribute has the potential to influence the general public. During war and other large-scale events, for example, people on the home front await reports from the front lines in order to evaluate the situation for themselves. The information must be carefully reviewed and free of personal opinion or exaggeration because it has the potential to cast an entire nation into panic. False or improper information may also cause harm to the public; it can sway political opinions, create enemies with other nations, or cause instability in the government.

You are a modern reporter who has been transported through time to medieval Scotland in order to compile a story on the murder of Duncan. Observe what you can from the characters involved with the event and record the answers to the fundamental questions of a reporter: who, what, when, where, how, and why? Once you've acquired those answers, write an article covering the event. Include a headline and be sure to keep the article factual and free of your own opinion.

Your first paragraph should be a condensed version of the event. The remainder of the article should contain any other significant information surrounding the murder; remember, in journalism, the *unanswered* questions are just as important as the answered questions.

Below is an example as to how your article might begin:

DUNCAN ASSASSINATED!

> INVERNESS. The calm after the battle was shattered today when Duncan, King of Scotland, was found murdered in the castle of General Macbeth. Also killed were two guards suspected of conducting the assassination. "O horror, horror, horror!" cried the shaken nobleman Macduff upon discovering the murdered Duncan.

Act II

Letter Writing

Objective: Writing to characters in the play

Activity

The violence in *Macbeth* is indeed brutal, but it's even worse because it is premeditated. Macbeth commits his atrocities knowing exactly what will happen to the victims. In Act II, we see Macbeth in his last few moments as an innocent man.

To complete this exercise, assume that you now have access to a message service that can reach Macbeth before he murders Duncan. Write a letter that will convince Macbeth to abandon his murderous scheme. In your letter, include anything that you know about Macbeth's life (spirituality, fears, etc.) that might make him change his mind.

After you write to Macbeth, write a letter to Duncan in case Macbeth cannot be swayed. Warn him of the plan and explain why Macbeth would do such a thing. Advise him on how to stay safe. Your letter must be believable because Duncan trusts Macbeth; it might be a good idea to keep it vague (don't identify the murderer—just the plan).

Examples:

> Wait, Macbeth!
>
> You already have the respect of everyone around you! Do not risk it all! You're a war hero and you own two provinces. You have no enemies in Scotland—why do you want to change that?

> Your Highness, the King of Scotland;
>
> Be warned, for a single man desires to kill you as you sleep this evening. He is one of your own trusted men; keep two vigilant guards with you at all times!

Act II

Letter Writing

Objective: Writing to characters in the play

Activity

The violence in *Macbeth* is indeed brutal, but it's even worse because it is premeditated. Macbeth commits his atrocities knowing exactly what will happen to the victims. In Act II, we see Macbeth in his last few moments as an innocent man.

To complete this exercise, assume that you now have access to a message service that can reach Macbeth before he murders Duncan. Write a letter that will convince Macbeth to abandon his murderous scheme. In your letter, include anything that you know about Macbeth's life (spirituality, fears, etc.) that might make him change his mind.

After you write to Macbeth, write a letter to Duncan in case Macbeth cannot be swayed. Warn him of the plan and explain why Macbeth would do such a thing. Advise him on how to stay safe. Your letter must be believable because Duncan trusts Macbeth; it might be a good idea to keep it vague (don't identify the murderer—just the plan).

Examples:

> Wait, Macbeth!
>
> You already have the respect of everyone around you! Do not risk it all! You're a war hero and you own two provinces. You have no enemies in Scotland—why do you want to change that?

> Your Highness, the King of Scotland;
>
> Be warned, for a single man desires to kill you as you sleep this evening. He is one of your own trusted men; keep two vigilant guards with you at all times!

Act III

Interviewing

Objective: Interviewing a main character

Activity

The new King Macbeth would provide an interesting interview, considering the traumatic events that accompanied his promotion.

You are a news-radio host popular for your interviews with people involved in scandals. You now have the chance to interview Macbeth, King of Scotland, on your talk-radio show. It will be an open mike show, and you will be taking calls from listeners.

Before the interview, you will want to research Macbeth a little in order to know what types of questions you'll be able to ask. You might want to question him about some of the events leading up to his crowning.

Remember, you are a talk-radio host. It is your job to pry the most interesting information from your guest so that listeners will continue to support you. Do not be afraid to unearth debatable issues that will draw phone calls. The public suspects some shady activity in the government, so you may want to question Macbeth on politics or how he feels about the prior King.

Divide the class into four groups. Each group will work together to produce a list of questions to ask Macbeth. The first question has been written for you.

Is there any truth to the rumor that you've been consulting witches?

What do you learn from them?

Do you believe the witches?

How is your marriage?

Do you and your wife get along well?

How do you feel about the way you became King of Scotland?

Do you have any idea of who could have murdered your good friend Duncan?

How does your wife feel about your recent promotion?

Note to teacher: As a follow up activity, students could dramatize the radio show, including the call-ins.

Act III

Interviewing

Objective: Interviewing a main character

Activity

The new King Macbeth would provide an interesting interview, considering the traumatic events that accompanied his promotion.

You are a news-radio host popular for your interviews with people involved in scandals. You now have the chance to interview Macbeth, King of Scotland, on your talk-radio show. It will be an open mike show, and you will be taking calls from listeners.

Before the interview, you will want to research Macbeth a little in order to know what types of questions you'll be able to ask. You might want to question him about some of the events leading up to his crowning.

Remember, you are a talk-radio host. It is your job to pry the most interesting information from your guest so that listeners will continue to support you. Do not be afraid to unearth debatable issues that will draw phone calls. The public suspects some shady activity in the government, so you may want to question Macbeth on politics or how he feels about the prior King.

Each group will work together to produce a list of questions to ask Macbeth. The first question has been written for you.

Is there any truth to the rumor that you've been consulting witches?

Act III

Interpreting Shakespeare

Objective: Interpreting the meaning of Shakespeare's language

Activity

In the third act, Lennox discusses the state of Scotland with another Lord:

Lennox: My former speeches have but hit your thoughts,
Which can interpret farther: only I say
Things have been strangely borne. The gracious Duncan
Was pitied of Macbeth: marry, he was dead:
And the right-valiant Banquo walk'd too late;
Whom, you may say, if't please you, Fleance kill'd,
For Fleance fled: men must not walk too late.
Who cannot want the thought, how monstrous
It was for Malcolm and for Donalbain
To kill their gracious father? damned fact!
How it did grieve Macbeth! did he not straight,
In pious rage, the two delinquents tear,
That were the slaves of drink and thralls of sleep?
Was not that nobly done? Ay, and wisely too;
For 'twould have anger'd any heart alive
To hear the men deny't. So that, I say,
He has borne all things well: and I do think
That, had he Duncan's sons under his key—
As, an't please heaven, he shall not—they should find
What 'twere to kill a father; so should Fleance.
But peace! for from broad words, and 'cause he fail'd
His presence at the tyrant's feast, I hear,
Macduff lives in disgrace: sir, can you tell
Where he bestows himself?

Rewrite Lennox's statement in your own words. Use modern English. When you complete the interpretation, explain the purpose of his statement.

Act III

Interpreting Shakespeare

Objective: Interpreting the meaning of Shakespeare's language

Activity

In the third act, Lennox discusses the state of Scotland with another Lord:

Lennox: My former speeches have but hit your thoughts,
Which can interpret farther: only I say
Things have been strangely borne. The gracious Duncan
Was pitied of Macbeth: marry, he was dead:
And the right-valiant Banquo walk'd too late;
Whom, you may say, if't please you, Fleance kill'd,
For Fleance fled: men must not walk too late.
Who cannot want the thought, how monstrous
It was for Malcolm and for Donalbain
To kill their gracious father? damned fact!
How it did grieve Macbeth! did he not straight,
In pious rage, the two delinquents tear,
That were the slaves of drink and thralls of sleep?
Was not that nobly done? Ay, and wisely too;
For 'twould have anger'd any heart alive
To hear the men deny't. So that, I say,
He has borne all things well: and I do think
That, had he Duncan's sons under his key—
As, an't please heaven, he shall not—they should find
What 'twere to kill a father; so should Fleance.
But peace! for from broad words, and 'cause he fail'd
His presence at the tyrant's feast, I hear,
Macduff lives in disgrace: sir, can you tell
Where he bestows himself?

Rewrite Lennox's statement in your own words. Use modern English. When you complete the
interpretation, explain the purpose of his statement.

Example:

Act III, Scene 6

Lennox: Everything I've said before, you can figure out for yourself.
I'm just saying that things are strange.

Macbeth felt sorry for Duncan; well, of course he felt sorry
for him—he was dead.

The valiant Banquo walked too late. Fleance fled, so
he obviously killed him—believe that if you want to;
after all, men must not walk too late.

And who can't humor the thought of how horrible it was
for Malcolm and Donalbain to kill their own dear father?
And how did Macbeth take it? In his dutiful rage did he not
stab two drunken, sleeping delinquents? Wasn't that noble?
Yes, and wise, too, because it only would have made people
mad to hear those men deny it.

Macbeth has done well, and I think that if he had Duncan's
sons in his grasp—heaven forbid—they would find out what killed their
father. Fleance, too.

But wait—I hear that Macduff is now disgraced because he
didn't go to the tyrant's feast. Do you know where he is?

Lennox is sarcastically explaining that Macbeth is most likely the murderer. He also
says that if Macbeth could get to Malcolm, Donalbain, and Fleance, he would probably
kill them, too. Lennox voices the growing sentiment against Macbeth at this point in the
play.

Example:

Act III, Scene 6

Lennox: Everything I've said before, you can figure out for yourself.
I'm just saying that things are strange.

Macbeth felt sorry for Duncan; well, of course he felt sorry
for him—he was dead.

Act IV

Alliteration

Objective: Recognizing alliteration

Activity

Alliteration may occur in numerous words in succession; however, many cases of alliteration in poetry involve only two successive words, and sometimes there may be a word separating the two alliterative words.

Alliteration is one of the several poetic devices that Shakespeare includes in his drama. In the first act we find "*Fair* is *Foul* and *Foul* is *Fair*. / Hover through the *fog* and *filthy* air." (Pg. 1)

Read through Act IV carefully and identify as many instances of alliteration as you can (at least ten). List each instance and cite the scene in which it appears. When you finish, write ten of your own alliterative phrases.

Examples:

Act I, Scene 3.	"rump-fed runyon"
Act I, Scene 5	"deep desires"
Act I, Scene 7	"false face"

1.

2.

3.

4.

5.

6.

7.

8.

9.

10.

Act IV

Alliteration

Objective: Recognizing alliteration

Activity

Alliteration may occur in numerous words in succession; however, many cases of alliteration in poetry involve only two successive words, and sometimes there may be a word separating the two alliterative words.

Alliteration is one of the several poetic devices that Shakespeare includes in his drama. In the first act we find "*F*air is *F*oul and *F*oul is *F*air. / Hover through the *f*og and *f*ilthy air." (Pg. 1)

Read through Act IV carefully and identify as many instances of alliteration as you can (at least ten). List each instance and cite the scene in which it appears. When you finish, write ten of your own alliterative phrases.

Examples:

Act I, Scene 3.	"rump-fed runyon"
Act I, Scene 5	"deep desires"
Act I, Scene 7	"false face"

1.

2.

3.

4.

5.

6.

7.

8.

9.

10.

Act IV

Communicating

Objective: Writing a speech
                     Speaking effectively

Activity

Macbeth is plagued with problems, but he is still the King of Scotland. By the end of Act IV, several prominent public figures are dead, and others are fleeing to England to build an army. Civil unrest is increasing, and rumors of a possible coup d'état take Macbeth to new levels of anxiety. Macbeth decides to address the people of Scotland in order to put them at ease.

Divide the class into small groups. Each group will act as Macbeth's staff, including chief advisors and speechwriters. Consult the text and each other to come up with the topics that Macbeth will need to address when he speaks to the people. Have one person list these topics. Using the list, each group should prepare a short speech for Macbeth (no more than three minutes).

While compiling the speech, remember to address all the major problems of Scotland according to the play. Also, try to ensure that the speech reflects Macbeth's personality (even if he's evil). In other words, Macbeth might not be entirely truthful about some of the events that he addresses.

When the speeches are complete, each group should have a volunteer stand up and read the speech to the class.

Example topics to include in the speech:

> *Why are people in the government being murdered?*

> *Who is behind the assassinations?*

> *Is the government of Scotland failing?*

> *Are we going to war with England?*

Act IV

Communicating

Objective: Writing a speech
                    Speaking effectively

Activity

Macbeth is plagued with problems, but he is still the King of Scotland. By the end of Act IV, several prominent public figures are dead, and others are fleeing to England to build an army. Civil unrest is increasing, and rumors of a possible coup d'état take Macbeth to new levels of anxiety. Macbeth decides to address the people of Scotland in order to put them at ease.

Divide the class into small groups. Each group will act as Macbeth's staff, including chief advisors and speechwriters. Consult the text and each other to come up with the topics that Macbeth will need to address when he speaks to the people. Have one person list these topics. Using the list, each group should prepare a short speech for Macbeth (no more than three minutes).

While compiling the speech, remember to address all the major problems of Scotland according to the play. Also, try to ensure that the speech reflects Macbeth's personality (even if he's evil). In other words, Macbeth might not be entirely truthful about some of the events that he addresses.

When the speeches are complete, each group should have a volunteer stand up and read the speech to the class.

Act V

Prophecy and Fate

Objective: Identifying plot consistencies

Activity

One of the themes in *Macbeth* is whether man has freewill or has control over his own destiny. The witches appear to govern the wicked events, but do they really? Once they reveal the prophecy (fate), must they maintain it or do they simply "enjoy the show"?

Macbeth takes the witch-prophecy quite seriously in Act I; so much, in fact, that he feels he has no choice but to pursue it. Once Macbeth changes his life to claim the part of the prophecy that benefits him, he begins to fear the prophecy. He knows that it has been accurate, so he worries about the remainder of the prophecy, which states that he will have no heirs.

Frightened, Macbeth unsuccessfully attempts to circumvent the prophecy. His attempts only hasten it. Fate appears to be predetermined and immovable.

Macbeth caused grave damage while trying to alter his fate; this is the reason why *Macbeth* is often called Shakespeare's bloodiest play. If fate was unalterable, do you think that Macbeth could have reached it without the bloodshed? Write a short paragraph and support your opinion. *Note to teacher: It is not necessary for this activity to be supported with quotations from the play.*

The **Fate Chart** on the next page contains a list of Macbeth's victims. Write in a sentence or two how each one dies and the Act and Scene in which it occurs. In the *Alternate Fate* column, explain how the prophecy could still come true if the character does not die. If saving a victim *would* change fate, describe an alternate future for that character.

The first character is done for you.

Act V

Prophecy and Fate

Objective: Identifying plot consistencies

Activity

One of the themes in *Macbeth* is whether man has freewill or has control over his own destiny. The witches appear to govern the wicked events, but do they really? Once they reveal the prophecy (fate), must they maintain it or do they simply "enjoy the show"?

Macbeth takes the witch-prophecy quite seriously in Act I; so much, in fact, that he feels he has no choice but to pursue it. Once Macbeth changes his life to claim the part of the prophecy that benefits him, he begins to fear the prophecy. He knows that it has been accurate, so he worries about the remainder of the prophecy, which states that he will have no heirs.

Frightened, Macbeth unsuccessfully attempts to circumvent the prophecy. His attempts only hasten it. Fate appears to be predetermined and immovable.

Macbeth caused grave damage while trying to alter his fate; this is the reason why *Macbeth* is often called Shakespeare's bloodiest play. If fate was unalterable, do you think that Macbeth could have reached it without the bloodshed? Write a short paragraph and support your opinion.

The **Fate Chart** on the next page contains a list of Macbeth's victims. Write in a sentence or two how each one dies and the Act and Scene in which it occurs. In the *Alternate Fate* column, explain how the prophecy could still come true if the character does not die. If saving a victim *would* change fate, describe an alternate future for that character.

The first character is done for you.

FATE CHART

Character	Nature of Death	Act, Scene	Alternate Fate
Duncan	Stabbing	2.2	If Duncan were to die of natural causes or even by someone other than Macbeth, Macbeth could still become the King.
Guards	*Stabbing*	*2.3*	*The guards are framed to cover Macbeth's crime. If they live, they would probably still be executed because of the evidence. If Macbeth didn't frame them, he would still become King.* *If alive, the guards could stop Macbeth from murdering Duncan and perhaps have Macbeth prosecuted. This would prevent Macbeth from acquiring the throne.*
Banquo	*Killed by cutthroats*	*3.3*	*If Banquo lives, Macbeth still remains King. Macbeth is also still in danger of Banquo's heirs taking the throne.*
Lady Macduff Son of Macduff	*Killed by cutthroats*	*4.3*	*Both Lady Macduff and her son could live and Macbeth would still remain King. These deaths, if anything, add to Macduff's rage when he kills Macbeth. Macbeth would probably still be overthrown if Macduff's family is left alive.*

FATE CHART

Character	Nature of Death	Act, Scene	Alternate Fate
Duncan	Stabbing	2.2	If Duncan were to die of natural causes or even by someone other than Macbeth, Macbeth could still become the King.

Acts I - V

Symbol

Objective: Interpreting symbols in the play

Activity

Blood is one example of a symbol in Macbeth. Prior to murdering Duncan, Macbeth imagines a bloody knife. After the murder, Macbeth's hands are bloody. Lady Macbeth is obsessed with the blood on her hands that never seems to disappear, and the bloody ghost of Banquo appears during Macbeth's dinner. Blood symbolizes murder or untimely death and the guilt that it causes.

Blood is only one of many symbols in *Macbeth*. The **Symbol Chart** supplies you with some of the other major symbols in the play. Review the play if necessary. Explain the meaning of each symbol and support your explanation with at least two references from the text. Note the act and scene in which you find your support.

When you finish the chart, identify two more symbols in *Macbeth* and explain them. Pay close attention to colors, numbers, and natural phenomena.

The first symbol has been completed for you.

Acts I - V

Symbol

Objective: Interpreting symbols in the play

Activity

Blood is one example of a symbol in Macbeth. Prior to murdering Duncan, Macbeth imagines a bloody knife. After the murder, Macbeth's hands are bloody. Lady Macbeth is obsessed with the blood on her hands that never seems to disappear, and the bloody ghost of Banquo appears during Macbeth's dinner. Blood symbolizes murder or untimely death and the guilt that it causes.

Blood is only one of many symbols in *Macbeth*. The **Symbol Chart** supplies you with some of the other major symbols in the play. Review the play if necessary. Explain the meaning of each symbol and support your explanation with at least two references from the text. Note the act and scene in which you find your support.

When you finish the chart, identify two more symbols in *Macbeth* and explain them. Pay close attention to colors, numbers, and natural phenomena.

The first symbol has been completed for you.

SYMBOL CHART

SYMBOL	Interpretation of Symbol	Supporting Evidence
Blood	Blood signifies murder and guilt.	Before murdering Duncan, Macbeth envisions a bloody dagger: "I see thee still; / And on thy blade and dudgeon gouts of blood" (Act II, Scene 1) "Here's the smell of the blood still: all the perfumes of Arabia will not sweeten this little hand." (Act V, Scene 1)
Owl	*The owl represents death, and it is symbolic of Macbeth.*	*The owl shrieks during the killing of Duncan: "It was the owl that shriek'd, the fatal bellman, / Which gives the stern'st good-night." (Act II, Scene 2)* *"On Tuesday last / A falcon towering in her pride of place / Was by a mousing owl hawk'd at and kill'd." (Act II, Scene 4)*
Sleep	*Sleep is symbolic of peace and innocence, but also death.* *[falcon is symbolic of the King]*	*By murdering Duncan as he sleeps, Macbeth effectively murders his innocence: "Glamis hath murder'd sleep, and therefore Cawdor / Shall sleep no more: Macbeth shall sleep no more." (Act II, Scene 2)* *In Act V, Scene 1, Lady Macbeth sleepwalks and reveals her connection to the murders. Only in sleep does her guilt appear.*
Night/ Darkness	*Evil, danger*	*"Come, seeling night, / Scarf up the tender eye of pitiful day" (Act III, Scene 2)* *"Come, thick night, / And pall thee in the dunnest smoke of hell, / That my keen knife see not the wound it makes, / Nor heaven peep through the blanket of the dark" (Act I, Scene 5)*
Snake	*Threat, danger*	*"look like the innocent flower, / But be the serpent under it" (Act I, Scene 5)* *"We have scotched the snake, not killed it." (Act III, Scene 2)*

SYMBOL CHART

SYMBOL	Interpretation of Symbol	Supporting Evidence
Blood	Blood signifies murder and guilt.	Before murdering Duncan, Macbeth envisions a bloody dagger: "I see thee still; / And on thy blade and dudgeon gouts of blood" (Act II, Scene 1) "Here's the smell of the blood still: all the perfumes of Arabia will not sweeten this little hand." (Act V, Scene 1)
Owl		
Sleep		
Night/ Darkness		
Snake		

Acts I – V

Creative Writing
Drawing

Objective: Identifying major themes and events in a drama

Activity

The old adage, "don't judge a book by its cover," is excellent advice; unfortunately, in modern culture, it is often the cover that first attracts potential customers to a book. *Macbeth* was first published in the seventeenth century, a time when books hardly required glossy, high-resolution graphics on the front and reviews from several major newspapers on the back in order to sell. Today, there are so many books on store shelves that flashy covers are necessary to seize attention long enough to capture readers' curiosity.

Imagine that *Macbeth* has just been written and that you work for Shakespeare's publisher. In order to catch the eye of consumers, the published play will need an effective jacket. It should command attention and at the same time truthfully portray the content of the play.

Divide the class into small groups. Within each group are two teams with the task of producing a new cover for *Macbeth*. The illustrators in the groups will draw or compile pictures for the front cover of the book. The cover art must include depictions of the story as well as the title and the author's name. The writers in the groups will write a review for the back cover that addresses the following questions:

1. What is the most interesting incident in the story? (Be careful not to give the story away.)
2. What are the themes of the play?
3. What does the story teach?
4. Why do you recommend this drama to other students?
5. Why is this a good drama for the classroom?

Acts I – V

Creative Writing
Drawing

Objective: Identifying major themes and events in a drama

Activity

The old adage, "don't judge a book by its cover," is excellent advice; unfortunately, in modern culture, it is often the cover that first attracts potential customers to a book. *Macbeth* was first published in the seventeenth century, a time when books hardly required glossy, high-resolution graphics on the front and reviews from several major newspapers on the back in order to sell. Today, there are so many books on store shelves that flashy covers are necessary to seize attention long enough to capture readers' curiosity.

Imagine that *Macbeth* has just been written and that you work for Shakespeare's publisher. In order to catch the eye of consumers, the published play will need an effective jacket. It should command attention and at the same time truthfully portray the content of the play.

Divide the class into small groups. Within each group are two teams with the task of producing a new cover for *Macbeth*. The illustrators in the groups will draw or compile pictures for the front cover of the book. The cover art must include depictions of the story as well as the title and the author's name. The writers in the groups will write a review for the back cover that addresses the following questions:

1. What is the most interesting incident in the story? (Be careful not to give the story away.)
2. What are the themes of the play?
3. What does the story teach?
4. Why do you recommend this drama to other students?
5. Why is this a good drama for the classroom?

Acts I - V

Characterization

Objective: Analyzing characters in the play

Activity

Psychiatrists are trained to examine patients, determine the source of problems, and implement possible solutions. The proper examination of a patient may require detailed information regarding the patient's family life and social environment. Using personal observations and facts gathered from the patient, the doctor makes a diagnosis.

You are now a modern psychiatrist, and below is a list of your patients for today. Write down your initial analysis for each patient and the possible cause of the problem. In the **TREATMENT** column, suggest a treatment. Remember, one character may have multiple disorders, each of which may require a different treatment.

PATIENT	PROBLEM	CAUSE	TREATMENT
8:00: Macbeth	Slave to spouse	Power-obsessed wife	Marital counseling
	Kills for his own benefit	Power-obsession	Rehabilitation
	Sees ghosts of victims	Guilt over murders	Reveal truth about murders; rehabilitation
9:00: Lady Macbeth	Obsessed with gaining power	Greed; low self-image	Heavy counseling; charity work
	Sleepwalks	Guilt over murders	Sleep clinic; medication
10:00: Fleance	Traumatized	Saw his father murdered	Counseling; medication
11:00: Banquo	Jealousy	Passed over for promotion	Reassurance about career
1:00: Macduff	Anger	Family was slaughtered	Group therapy
2:00: Ross	Anxiety	Realizes that Macbeth is the murderer	Counseling; relaxation exercises

Acts I - V

Characterization

Objective: Analyzing characters in the play

Activity

Psychiatrists are trained to examine patients, determine the source of problems, and implement possible solutions. The proper examination of a patient may require detailed information regarding the patient's family life and social environment. Using personal observations and facts gathered from the patient, the doctor makes a diagnosis.

You are now a modern psychiatrist, and below is a list of your patients for today. Write down your initial analysis for each patient and the possible cause of the problem. In the **TREATMENT** column, suggest a treatment. Remember, one character may have multiple disorders, each of which may require a different treatment.

PATIENT	PROBLEM	CAUSE	TREATMENT
8:00: Macbeth			
9:00: Lady Macbeth			
10:00: Fleance			
11:00: Banquo			
1:00: Macduff			
2:00: Ross			

Acts I – V

Understanding Shakespeare's Language

Objective: Understanding Elizabethan English

Activity

Rewrite the following script in Shakespeare's dialect so that it would make sense to characters in the play. Remember to change items in the dialogue to fit Shakespeare's time period.

> *Scene: Small town. Two policemen respond to a car accident. A woman stands on the road yelling for help.*

Woman: Hey, over here! Over here! Hurry!

Officer 1:   Ma'am, calm down, calm down. Are you hurt?

Woman: No, no, I'm fine. It's that van over there; it's on fire and there's still a woman and kid inside!

Officer 2:   Go over by the car, where it's safe.

The two officers run to the van

Officer 1:   Lady, can you hear me? Can you get out?

Officer 2:   She's knocked out; the seatbelt's holding her inside!

Officer 1:   I can reach the kid—I've got the kid; get the woman!

Officer 2:   Ma'am, can you hear me? Ma'am?

Officer1 holds child and turns

Officer 1:   Take my knife and cut her free! The fire's getting worse!

Officer 2 grabs knife; Officer 1 takes child to safety

Woman (woozy): Where am I? (coughs)

Officer 1:   Hold still ma'am, I've got to cut you free.

Officer 1 frees the woman and pulls her from the van

Acts I – V

Understanding Shakespeare's Language

Objective: Understanding Elizabethan English

Activity

Rewrite the following script in Shakespeare's dialect so that it would make sense to characters in the play. Remember to change items in the dialogue to fit Shakespeare's time period.

Scene: Small town. Two policemen respond to a car accident. A woman stands on the road yelling for help.

Woman: Hey, over here! Over here! Hurry!

Officer 1: Ma'am, calm down, calm down. Are you hurt?

Woman: No, no, I'm fine. It's that van over there; it's on fire and there's still a woman and kid inside!

Officer 2: Go over by the car, where it's safe.

The two officers run to the van

Officer 1: Lady, can you hear me? Can you get out?

Officer 2: She's knocked out; the seatbelt's holding her inside!

Officer 1: I can reach the kid—I've got the kid; get the woman!

Officer 2: Ma'am, can you hear me? Ma'am?

Officer1 holds child and turns

Officer 1: Take my knife and cut her free! The fire's getting worse!

Officer 2 grabs knife; Officer 1 takes child to safety

Woman (woozy): Where am I? (coughs)

Officer 1: Hold still ma'am, I've got to cut you free.

Officer 1 frees the woman and pulls her from the van

We have begun the script for you:

Scene: Castle just outside a village; two knights help a noblewoman whose carriage has been overturned and set on fire by thieves. A servant woman calls for help.

Woman: Here sires, please, with haste!

Knight 1:   *Peace, woman; what ails you?*

Woman: *The carriage afar—the pyre; a mother and child lay trapped within!*

Knight 2:   *Get thee to cover.*

The knights run to the burning carriage.

Knight 1:   *M'lady, doest thou hear? Thou'rt free?*

Knight 2:   *The lady sleeps! Her harness retains her!*

Knight 1:   *The babe is I' reach—I've the child; retrieve the dame!*

Knight 2:   *M'lady, doest thou wake?*

Knight 1:   *The blazes increase; taketh my dagger and deliver her!*

Lady: *Where?*

Knight 1:   *Be still madam, whilst I cut you from thy harness.*

We have begun the script for you:

Scene: Castle just outside a village; two knights help a noblewoman whose carriage has been overturned and set on fire by thieves. A servant woman calls for help.

Woman: Here sires, please, with haste!

Knight 1:

Woman:

Knight 2:

Knight 1:

Knight 2:

Knight 1:

Knight 2:

Knight 1:

Lady:

Knight 1:

Acts I – V

Plot

Objective: Relating conflicts and characters in *Macbeth* to contemporary conflicts

Activity

Shakespeare's drama is often described as universal, meaning it appeals to all audiences and cultures anywhere in history. Shakespeare achieves this universal appeal by using age-old themes to which anyone can relate, regardless of time or geography. *Romeo and Juliet,* for example, portrays lovers whose families are enemies—a story that could take place as easily in present-day America as it could in medieval Europe.

Consider the storyline of *Macbeth* and think of where or how it could occur in the present day. Be sure to take into account the many unpredictable organizations that exist in the world: governments (including monarchies like Macbeth's), corporations, organized crime families, etc.

Once you have identified a situation that parallels *Macbeth*, fill in the supplied chart, **The Modern *Macbeth***, with the equivalent events and characters. Several examples have been completed for you. These need be only short comments.

Acts I – V

Plot

Objective: Relating conflicts and characters in *Macbeth* to contemporary conflicts

Activity

Shakespeare's drama is often described as universal, meaning it appeals to all audiences and cultures anywhere in history. Shakespeare achieves this universal appeal by using age-old themes to which anyone can relate, regardless of time or geography. *Romeo and Juliet,* for example, portrays lovers whose families are enemies—a story that could take place as easily in present-day America as it could in medieval Europe.

Consider the storyline of *Macbeth* and think of where or how it could occur in the present day. Be sure to take into account the many unpredictable organizations that exist in the world: governments (including monarchies like Macbeth's), corporations, organized crime families, etc.

Once you have identified a situation that parallels *Macbeth*, fill in the supplied chart, **The Modern *Macbeth***, with the equivalent events and characters. Several examples have been completed for you. These need be only short comments.

THE MODERN *MACBETH*

Original *Macbeth*	Alternate *Macbeth* (Today)
SETTING	
Scotland *Kingdom* *Inverness* *Castle Macbeth*	United States *Large corporation* *New York City* *Mansion of executive*
PLOT	
Man murders King and takes the throne *Man gets idea from witches* *Man gains support from a power-hungry wife*	Executive murders boss to take over company *Man gets idea from phone-psychics* *Executive gets support from a power-hungry wife*
CHARACTERS	
Duncan: King of Scotland Macbeth: *General in Scottish Army; potential future heir to throne* Banquo: *fellow general* Macduff: *Account executive*	CEO of corporation *Vice-president of corporation; next-in-line for promotion* *Fellow vice-president* *Assistant vice-president*
ACTION	
Macbeth kills Duncan *Macbeth kills guards to mask the crime* *Macbeth kills Banquo, his competition* *Macbeth kills family of Macduff*	Executive kills CEO *Executive kills security guards to mask the crime* *Executive kills fellow VP, his competition* *Executive kills family of assistant VP*

THE MODERN *MACBETH*

Original *Macbeth*	Alternate *Macbeth* (Today)
SETTING	
Scotland	United States
PLOT	
Man murders King and takes the throne	Executive murders boss to take over company
CHARACTERS	
Duncan: King of Scotland	CEO of corporation
ACTION	
Macbeth kills Duncan	Executive kills CEO

Acts I – V

Characterization

Objective: Creating a character map

Activity

Character relationships vary within and at the end of each Act.   For each Act, draw a map that depicts the relationships among the characters. Use the following key:

⟶ An arrow from one character to another depicts a friendship.

⟷ A double arrow indicates mutual friendship.

------▶ A broken arrow indicates dislike.

◀-----▶ A double broken arrow indicates mutual dislike.

( ) Parenthesis around a name indicate that a character is no longer present. (character is absent or dead)

? A question mark means that the reader is unsure at that point.

Example:

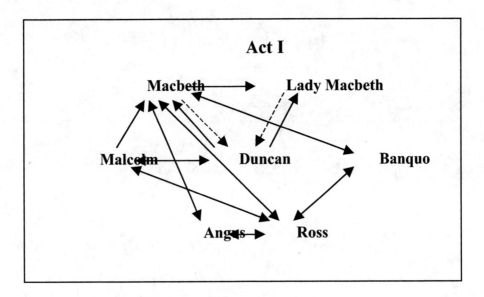

Acts I – V

Characterization

Objective: Creating a character map

Activity

Character relationships vary within and at the end of each Act. For each Act, draw a map that depicts the relationships among the characters. Use the following key:

───────▶ An arrow from one character to another depicts a friendship.

◀──────▶ A double arrow indicates mutual friendship.

------▶ A broken arrow indicates dislike.

◀-----▶ A double broken arrow indicates mutual dislike.

[   ] Parenthesis around a name indicate that a character is no longer present. (character is absent or dead)

? A question mark means that the reader is unsure at that point.

Example:

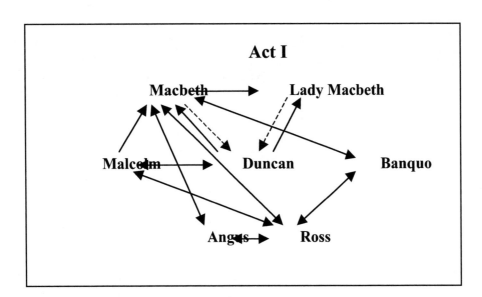

Act II

Act III

Act II

Act III

Act IV

Act V

Act IV

Act V

Acts I - V

Resume Writing

Objective: Interpreting details from the text

Activity

Attached is a sample resume. Notice that the resume includes career objectives, prior work experience, skills, personal interests, and references.

Weary of being King, Macbeth has decided to pursue a new career. Overlooking his criminal record and death, write a resume for Macbeth or Lady Macbeth.

Your first task will be to think up a career for a person of Macbeth's experience to pursue. Identifying that will allow you to write the resume so that it is targeted to a specific job.

A blank resume is attached, but feel free to use a computer if you have one available.

Acts I - V

Resume Writing

Objective: Interpreting details from the text

Activity

Attached is a sample resume. Notice that the resume includes career objectives, prior work experience, skills, personal interests, and references.

Weary of being King, Macbeth has decided to pursue a new career. Overlooking his criminal record and death, write a resume for Macbeth or Lady Macbeth.

Your first task will be to think up a career for a person of Macbeth's experience to pursue. Identifying that will allow you to write the resume so that it is targeted to a specific job.

A blank resume is attached, but feel free to use a computer if you have one available.

MACBETH

OBJECTIVE

To find a rewarding position as general of feudal army

EXPERIENCE

1030? – Present   *Government of Scotland*
General of Forces
- *Swiftly suppressed Norweyan uprising*
- *Disemboweled and decapitated leader of opposing forces*
- *Responsible for $10,000 profit from Norweyan King*

1045?–Present   *Government of Scotland*   *Scotland*
Thane of Glamis
- *Maintained dual ownership of territory with King of Scotland*

1051?-Present   *Government of Scotland*   *Scotland*
Thane of Cawdor
- *Maintained dual ownership of territory with King of Scotland*

INTERESTS

Consulting witches, usurping thrones; desire for power and total control

REFERENCES

Duncan. King of Scotland

Banquo. General of Scottish Forces

Macduff, the Noble. Fife.

CASTLE MACBETH
INVERNESS, SCOTLAND
MACBETH@BAGPIPES.COM

EXAMPLE: MACBETH

OBJECTIVE

To find a rewarding position as general of feudal army

EXPERIENCE

1030? – Present   *Government of Scotland*
General of Forces
- *Swiftly suppressed Norweyan uprising*
- *Disemboweled and decapitated leader of opposing forces*
- *Responsible for $10,000 profit from Norweyan King*

1045?–Present Government of Scotland   *Scotland*
Thane of Glamis
- *Maintained dual ownership of territory with King of Scotland*

1051?-Present Government of Scotland   *Scotland*
Thane of Cawdor
- *Maintained dual ownership of territory with King of Scotland*

INTERESTS

Consulting witches, usurping thrones; desire for power and total control

REFERENCES

Duncan. King of Scotland

Banquo. General of Scottish Forces

Macduff, the Noble. Fife.

HECATE

OBJECTIVE

A challenging position in a small coven as senior witch

EXPERIENCE

650? – Present   *Scotland*
Senior Witch

- *Supervised three witches in performance of supernatural duties*
- *Enhanced spell effectiveness on Scottish general*
  - *Directly contributed to five wrongful-deaths*
  - *Drove ambitious Queen to madness*
- *Evaluated quality of witch-brew*
- *Directed evil music during spell-casting events*
- *Summoned apparitions to ensure complete manipulation of fate*

INTERESTS

Tampering with the fate of government and military officials; making brew; causing general chaos and discontent.

REFERENCES

Macbeth. Former King of Scotland. Customer.

Three witches in Scotland. (Names available upon request)

HECATE
SCOTLAND
WITCH47@HIGHLANDS.COM

HECATE

OBJECTIVE

A challenging position in a small coven as senior witch

EXPERIENCE

650? – Present   *Scotland*
Senior Witch

- *Supervised three witches in performance of supernatural duties*
- *Enhanced spell effectiveness on Scottish general*
  - *Directly contributed to five wrongful-deaths*
  - *Drove ambitious Queen to madness*
- *Evaluated quality of witch-brew*
- *Directed evil music during spell-casting events*
- *Summoned apparitions to ensure complete manipulation of fate*

INTERESTS

Tampering with the fate of government and military officials; making brew; causing general chaos and discontent.

REFERENCES

Macbeth. Former King of Scotland. Customer.

Three witches in Scotland. (Names available upon request)

MACBETH

OBJECTIVE

EXPERIENCE

INTERESTS

REFERENCES

CASTLE MACBETH
INVERNESS, SCOTLAND
MACBETH@BAGPIPES.COM

MACBETH

OBJECTIVE _____

EXPERIENCE _____

_____

INTERESTS _____

REFERENCES _____

CASTLE MACBETH
INVERNESS, SCOTLAND
MACBETH@BAGPIPES.COM

LADY MACBETH

OBJECTIVE

EXPERIENCE

INTERESTS

REFERENCES

CASTLE MACBETH
INVERNESS, SCOTLAND
MACBETH@BAGPIPES.COM

LADY MACBETH

OBJECTIVE
_____

EXPERIENCE
_____

_____

INTERESTS
_____

REFERENCES
_____

CASTLE MACBETH
INVERNESS, SCOTLAND
MACBETH@BAGPIPES.COM

Acts I – V

Acting

Objective: Understanding drama through performance

Activity

Plays such as *Macbeth* are written for the stage. Reading a play without watching it sometimes omits elements that only a physical performance would introduce.

Divide the class into small groups. Each group should select a single scene from *Macbeth* to act out for the class. The groups should first discuss the chosen scenes and settle on the details that the scene will require (voice, stage positions, mood, volume, etc.).

Members of each group will assign themselves roles. The members of the group should divide the scene to accommodate everyone; for example, two people will act the first half of the scene, and the others will act the second half.

Groups may also choose soliloquies, but no one in the group should do the same soliloquy. In addition, the group should still discuss the dramatic details of the chosen material.

If scheduling permits, students should memorize the material to be performed. When the groups are ready, perform the scenes for the rest of the class. Conduct a brief discussion after each scene to determine whether the class feels that the scene was performed so that the meaning is apparent.

Acts I – V

Acting

Objective: Understanding drama through performance

Activity

Plays such as *Macbeth* are written for the stage. Reading a play without watching it sometimes omits elements that only a physical performance would introduce.

Divide the class into small groups. Each group should select a single scene from *Macbeth* to act out for the class. The groups should first discuss the chosen scenes and settle on the details that the scene will require (voice, stage positions, mood, volume, etc.).

Members of each group will assign themselves roles. The members of the group should divide the scene to accommodate everyone; for example, two people will act the first half of the scene, and the others will act the second half.

Groups may also choose soliloquies, but no one in the group should do the same soliloquy. In addition, the group should still discuss the dramatic details of the chosen material.

If scheduling permits, students should memorize the material to be performed. When the groups are ready, perform the scenes for the rest of the class. Conduct a brief discussion after each scene to determine whether the class feels that the scene was performed so that the meaning is apparent.

Wrap-up

Metaphor

Objective: Recognizing and interpreting metaphors

Activity

Macbeth contains many instances of metaphors. The **METAPHOR CHART** lists ten examples. On the chart, explain the significance or meaning of each of the examples. When you've finished, find four more examples of metaphor and repeat the process. Be sure to list the act and scene where you find your example.

The first metaphor is completed for you.

Wrap-up

Metaphor

Objective: Recognizing and interpreting metaphors

Activity

Macbeth contains many instances of metaphors. The **METAPHOR CHART** lists ten examples. On the chart, explain the significance or meaning of each of the examples. When you've finished, find four more examples of metaphor and repeat the process. Be sure to list the act and scene where you find your example.

The first metaphor is completed for you.

METAPHOR CHART

Metaphor	Act, Scene	Explanation of Metaphor
"Fair is foul, and foul is fair."	1.1	The witches are evil; to them, good is bad and bad is good.
"The spring, the head, the fountain of your blood / Is stopp'd; the very source of it is stopp'd"	2.3	*When Duncan dies, he can produce no more sons. He is like a fountain or spring that stops flowing.*
"Duncan is in his grave; / After life's fitful fever he sleeps well"	3.2	*The "fitful fever" is the evil murder to which Duncan fell victim when he was still alive. It also can be interpreted as meaning that after life's difficulties, Duncan finally is at peace.*
"Let's make us medicines of our great revenge, / To cure this deadly grief."	4.3	*Malcolm likens a plan for revenge to medicine. Instead of curing a sickness, this "medicine" will counter grief.*
"Your son, my lord, has paid a soldier's debt"	5.8	*Young Siward, a soldier, died. Soldiers bear the risk of death in any given battle. Some of them "pay," like Siward.*
"that we but teach / Blood instructions, which being taught return / To plague th' inventor"	1.7	*Macbeth's actions are bloody, and they will eventually kill him. [this is also foreshadowing]*
"The wine of life is drawn, and the mere lees / is left this vault to brag of."	2.3	*The pleasure of life is gone; Macbeth compares his life to an empty wine cask.*
"There the grown serpent lies; the worm that's fled / Hath mature that in time will venom breed"	3.4	*Macbeth likens Banquo to a serpent. Fleance is the younger snake, and he will produce more snakes that will endanger Macbeth.*

METAPHOR CHART

Metaphor	Act, Scene	Explanation of Metaphor
"Fair is foul, and foul is fair."	1.1	The witches are evil; to them, good is bad and bad is good.
"The spring, the head, the fountain of your blood / Is stopp'd; the very source of it is stopp'd"	2.3	
"Duncan is in his grave; / After life's fitful fever he sleeps well"	3.2	
"Let's make us medicines of our great revenge, / To cure this deadly grief."	4.3	
"Your son, my lord, has paid a soldier's debt"	5.8	
"that we but teach / Blood instructions, which being taught return / To plague th' inventor"	1.7	
"The wine of life is drawn, and the mere lees / is left this vault to brag of."	2.3	
"There the grown serpent lies; the worm that's fled / Hath mature that in time will venom breed"	3.4	

"Hold fast the mortal sword, and like good men / Bestride our down-fall'n birthdom"	4.3	*Macduff refers to courage or valor as a sword that will help to restore the kingdom.*
"Life's but a walking shadow, a poor player / That struts and frets his hour upon the stage / And then is heard no more: it is a tale / Told by an idiot, full of sound and fury, / Signifying nothing."	5.5	*Life is a play in which people are poor actors. No matter how they over-dramatize, they will ultimately be forgotten. To Macbeth, life is meaningless*

"Hold fast the mortal sword, and like good men / Bestride our down-fall'n birthdom"	4.3	
"Life's but a walking shadow, a poor player / That struts and frets his hour upon the stage / And then is heard no more: it is a tale / Told by an idiot, full of sound and fury, / Signifying nothing."	5.5	

Wrap-up

Writing to Shakespeare

Objective: Communicating with the author

Activity

In the space below, write a letter to Shakespeare to give him your thoughts on *Macbeth*. Include references to specific acts and scenes to help describe your likes or dislikes in the play.

Include any questions that you may have regarding the play itself, the language, or the creation of the play. Be sure to offer any advice that you think might help Shakespeare improve the play [for contemporary audiences.]

The letter is started for you.

Dear Mr. Shakespeare,

     I've just finished reading *Macbeth*, and I have a few questions and comments for you.
     In Act III, Scene III, the dying Banquo tells Fleance, "Thou mayst revenge." Fleance then hides for the remainder of the play. Was Fleance originally supposed to return to act upon his father's wish?

Wrap-up

Writing to Shakespeare

Objective: Communicating with the author

Activity

In the space below, write a letter to Shakespeare to give him your thoughts on *Macbeth*. Include references to specific acts and scenes to help describe your likes or dislikes in the play.

Include any questions that you may have regarding the play itself, the language, or the creation of the play. Be sure to offer any advice that you think might help Shakespeare improve the play [for contemporary audiences.]

The letter is started for you.

Dear Mr. Shakespeare,

      I've just finished reading *Macbeth*, and I have a few questions and comments for you. In Act III, Scene III, the dying Banquo tells Fleance, "Thou mayst revenge." Fleance then hides for the remainder of the play. Was Fleance originally supposed to return to act upon his father's wish?

Wrap-up

Plot

Objective: Creating a graph that depicts the action of the play

Activity

The intensity of some literature and drama follows a pattern: it rises and then falls. If one were to create a timeline and label the stages of this pattern, it might look like this:

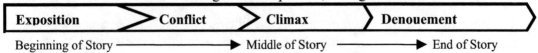

In this pattern, the intensity of the story is lowest at the beginning and end and highest during the climax. This pattern may or may not apply to *Macbeth*.

Most businesses today use charts and graphs to visually represent their activity over a given period of time. You can use the same method to represent the activity, or intensity, of *Macbeth*.

Create a graph that portrays the level of activity in *Macbeth* to the time at which it occurs. The bottom should be divided by acts, while the side should be divided by the intensity of the action in the play. The result will be a line graph that illustrates the rise and fall of action throughout the play.

We have provided a list of events to place on your chart. After you place them, connect them to form a line graph. Three events have been placed for you.

When you finish your graph, identify any patterns in the intensity of the play. Compare your graph to those of your classmates and discuss any outstanding similarities or differences.

Put the following events in their proper places on the chart:

- Macbeth crowned
- Banquo murdered
- Hecate scolds witches
- Guards murdered

Lady Macbeth dies
- Lennox warns Lady Macduff
- Malcolm announces crowning
- Macduff's family murdered
- Porter answers door

- Macduff learns of murdered family
- Macbeth's head brought forth
- Army reaches Dunsinane
- Macbeth fights Macduff
- Ghost of Banquo appears
- Malcom and Macduff plot
- Witches' first prophecy
- Macbeth sees apparitions

Wrap-up

Plot

Objective: Creating a graph that depicts the action of the play

Activity

The intensity of some literature and drama follows a pattern: it rises and then falls. If one were to create a timeline and label the stages of this pattern, it might look like this:

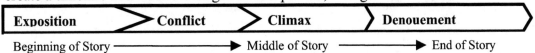

In this pattern, the intensity of the story is lowest at the beginning and end and highest during the climax. This pattern may or may not apply to *Macbeth*.

Most businesses today use charts and graphs to visually represent their activity over a given period of time. You can use the same method to represent the activity, or intensity, of *Macbeth*.

Create a graph that portrays the level of activity in *Macbeth* to the time at which it occurs. The bottom should be divided by acts, while the side should be divided by the intensity of the action in the play. The result will be a line graph that illustrates the rise and fall of action throughout the play.

We have provided a list of events to place on your chart. After you place them, connect them to form a line graph. Three events have been placed for you.

When you finish your graph, identify any patterns in the intensity of the play. Compare your graph to those of your classmates and discuss any outstanding similarities or differences.

Level of Intensity

Low   High

ACT I	ACT II	ACT III	ACT IV	ACT V

- Duncan murdered

- Witches brew

- Lady Macbeth sleepwalks

Put the following events in their proper places on the chart:

- Macbeth crowned
- Banquo murdered
- Hecate scolds witches
- Guards murdered
- Lady Macbeth dies
- Lennox warns Lady Macduff
- Malcolm announces crowning
- Macduff's family murdered
- Porter answers door

- Macduff learns of murdered family
- Macbeth's head brought forth
- Army reaches Dunsinane
- Macbeth fights Macduff
- Ghost of Banquo appears
- Malcom and Macduff plot
- Witches' first prophecy
- Macbeth sees apparitions

Example:

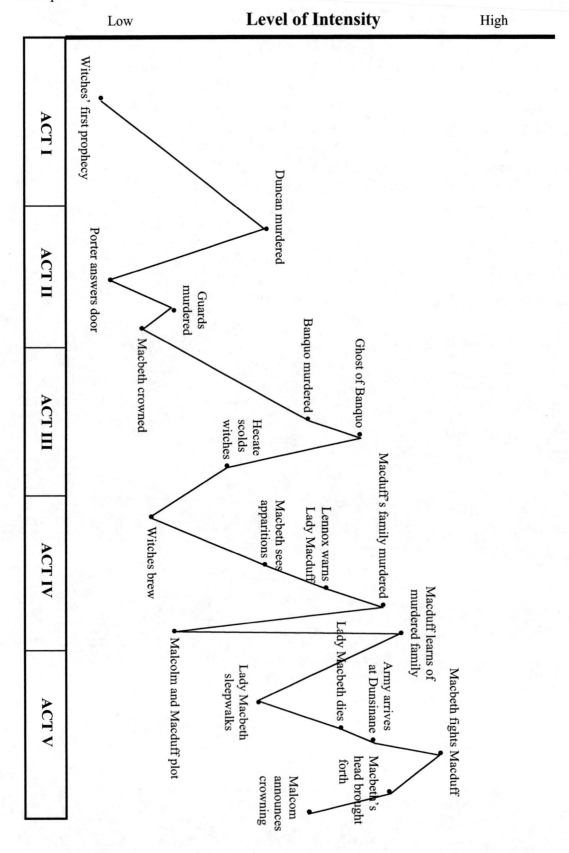

Low   **Level of Intensity**   High

ACT I

Witches' first prophecy

Duncan murdered

ACT II

Porter answers door

Guards murdered

Macbeth crowned

Banquo murdered

Ghost of Banquo

ACT III

Hecate scolds witches

Macbeth sees apparitions

Lennox warns Lady Macduff

Macduff's family murdered

ACT IV

Witches brew

Macduff learns of murdered family

Lady Macbeth dies

Army arrives at Dunsinane

Macbeth fights Macduff

ACT V

Malcolm and Macduff plot

Lady Macbeth sleepwalks

Malcom announces crowning

Macbeth's head brought forth

Level of Intensity

Low   High

ACT I	ACT II	ACT III	ACT IV	ACT V

• Duncan murdered

• Witches brew

• Lady Macbeth sleepwalks

Wrap-up

Setting and Story

Objective: Creating a map of the action in the play

Activity

Like many of Shakespeare's dramas, *Macbeth*—while not entirely true—is based on real events in world history. A Duncan and a Macbeth once really existed in Scotland, though not exactly as Shakespeare portrays.

The characters in *Macbeth* may be only based on fact, but the places in *Macbeth* are (or once were) certainly real. Examine the map on the next page, and you'll find some of the places that comprise the setting of the play. Use the lines, arrows, and symbols in the legend to put the major landmarks and events of the play on the places in which they occur.

Wrap-up

Setting and Story

Objective: Creating a map of the action in the play

Activity

Like many of Shakespeare's dramas, *Macbeth*—while not entirely true—is based on real events in world history. A Duncan and a Macbeth once really existed in Scotland, though not exactly as Shakespeare portrays.

The characters in *Macbeth* may be only based on fact, but the places in *Macbeth* are (or once were) certainly real. Examine the map on the next page, and you'll find some of the places that comprise the setting of the play. Use the lines, arrows, and symbols in the legend to put the major landmarks and events of the play on the places in which they occur.

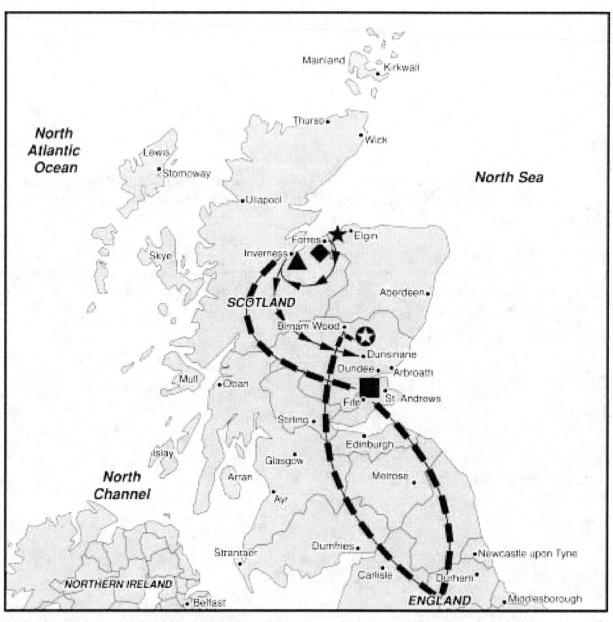

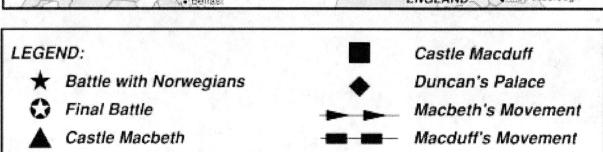

LEGEND:

★ **Battle with Norwegians**

✪ **Final Battle**

▲ **Castle Macbeth**

■ **Castle Macduff**

◆ **Duncan's Palace**

▶▶ **Macbeth's Movement**

■■ **Macduff's Movement**

North Atlantic Ocean

North Sea

North Channel

Mainland · Kirkwall

Thurso · · Wick

Lewis
· Stornoway

· Ullapool

SCOTLAND

Skye

Forres · · Elgin
Inverness ·

Aberdeen ·

Birnam Wood ·

Dunsinane ·
Dundee · · Arbroath

Mull
· Oban

Fife · · St. Andrews

Stirling ·

Edinburgh ·

Islay

Glasgow ·

Melrose ·

Arran

Ayr ·

Dumfries ·

Stranraer ·

Newcastle upon Tyne ·

NORTHERN IRELAND

· Belfast

Carlisle ·

Durham ·

ENGLAND · Middlesborough

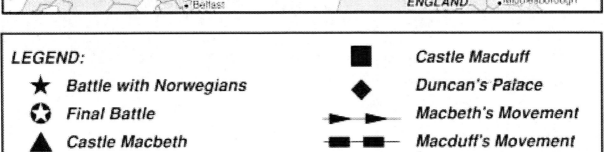

LEGEND:

★ Battle with Norwegians

✪ Final Battle

▲ Castle Macbeth

■ Castle Macduff

◆ Duncan's Palace

▶▶ Macbeth's Movement

■■ Macduff's Movement

Wrap-up

Changing Plot

Objective: Bringing Shakespeare to the box office

Activity

You are now a major movie director who wants to make a film called *Macbeth: The Movie*. *Macbeth* has been put on the screen before, but you are going to turn it into a blockbuster. It may be set in the past, present, or future, and it will contain modern English. The script is somewhat consistent with the original *Macbeth*, but you, along with the writers, need to make a few changes in order to make the movie more appealing. They are:

1. Macbeth must be a woman instead of a man; Lady Macbeth [renamed] is a man.

2. Banquo is the brother of Macbeth.

3. Fleance gets to avenge his father.

4. Change the setting

5. Malcolm is as evil as Macbeth.

6. The play must have a happy ending.

Write a one-page synopsis of the movie that includes your changes. When you finish, choose the cast for the included list of major characters. Use living actors, and try to select the perfect person for each part.

Use the next page to write your synopsis. An example paragraph and a list of characters is provided for you.

Wrap-up

Changing Plot

Objective: Bringing Shakespeare to the box office

Activity

You are now a major movie director who wants to make a film called *Macbeth: The Movie*. *Macbeth* has been put on the screen before, but you are going to turn it into a blockbuster. It may be set in the past, present, or future, and it will contain modern English. The script is somewhat consistent with the original *Macbeth*, but you, along with the writers, need to make a few changes in order to make the movie more appealing. They are:

1. Macbeth must be a woman instead of a man; Lady Macbeth [renamed] is a man.

2. Banquo is the brother of Macbeth.

3. Fleance gets to avenge his father.

4. Change the setting

5. Malcolm is as evil as Macbeth.

6. The play must have a happy ending.

Write a one-page synopsis of the movie that includes your changes. When you finish, choose the cast for the included list of major characters. Use living actors, and try to select the perfect person for each part.

Use the next page to write your synopsis. An example paragraph and a list of characters is provided for you.
Example:

The movie opens at Mars mining colony delta-twelve, three months after a decade-long campaign against a rogue colony of ore-raiders. Vice-commander Susan Macbeth, known for her effective battle tactics, is now contemplating her next career move, thanks to secret dealings with some of the exiles living on the edge of the colony. After eight years of number-two status and wages, she is ready to relieve Colonel Duncan, delta-twelve commander, whether he is ready to retire or not.

Example:

The movie opens at Mars mining colony delta-twelve, three months after a decade-long campaign against a rogue colony of ore-raiders. Vice-commander Susan Macbeth, known for her effective battle tactics, is now contemplating her next career move, thanks to secret dealings with some of the exiles living on the edge of the colony. After eight years of number-two status and wages, she is ready to relieve Colonel Duncan, delta-twelve commander, whether he is ready to retire or not.

Susan's husband, Larry Macbeth, has been pushing Susan to pursue her endeavors, especially after receiving an "anonymous" gift of five thousand colony credits shortly after discovering Susan speaking with the exiles, whose efforts to gain acknowledgement in the colony were never on Colonel Duncan's priority list.

Susan Macbeth takes her first step to the top when she, assisted by Larry, tampers with a computer and causes Duncan to be stranded in an airlock at the foundry. Duncan suffocates after using up his air supply, and the supposed malfunction is quickly contributed to two maintenance technicians on duty during the time of Duncan's death.

Major Banquo, the colony security officer, is never convinced that Duncan's death is accidental. To stop Banquo's investigation, Susan Macbeth hires three exiles to murder him. The exiles kill Banquo, but his son, Fleance, gets away and tells Duncan's son, Malcolm, what happened.

Malcolm and Fleance, suspecting treachery on behalf of Susan Macbeth, plot to remove her from her new job as commander. Fleance wants Susan to be tried in court, but Malcolm seeks only to avenge his father by killing Susan. While gathering evidence in Macbeth's office one evening, the sons encounter Susan and Larry Macbeth. A fight ensues, and Fleance kills Susan in self-defense. Larry escapes, but Malcom chases him down and executes him, originally for revenge, but also because Larry once witnessed Malcolm conducting illegal trade with the raiders.

CAST:

Susan Macbeth: Larry Macbeth:

Duncan: Malcolm:

Banquo: Fleance:

Donalbain: Macduff:

Lennox: Ross:

CAST:

Susan Macbeth: Larry Macbeth:

Duncan: Malcolm:

Banquo: Fleance:

Donalbain: Macduff:

Lennox: Ross:

Wrap-up

Emotions

Objective: Finding quotes that portray emotions

Activity

Macbeth is known for its intensity as a drama. For the duration of the play, characters are in a perpetual fight for survival. By murdering friends and enemies alike, Macbeth maintains an environment in which no character appears to be safe from harm.

The intense nature of *Macbeth* makes it a very emotional play. The **Emotion Chart** below contains a list of emotions depicted in the text. The location of each emotion is provided for you. Using the locations, find the source of each emotion. Identify the proper characters and quote them on the chart. The first entry has been completed for you.

Emotion Chart

Emotion	Source (character)	Act. Scene	Quote
Fear	Macbeth	1	"There is none but he / whose being I do fear"
Hatred	*Macduff*	5.8	*"My voice is in my sword, thou bloodier villain / Than terms can give thee out!"*
Guilt	*Macbeth*	2.2	*"I am afraid to think what I have done; / Look on't again I dare not."*
Anxiety	*Macbeth*	3.4	*"Then comes my fit again . . . I am cabin'd, cribb'd, confined, bound in / To saucy doubts and fears."*
Love	*Macbeth (letter)*	1.5	*"my dearest partner of greatness"*
Wrath	*Macduff*	4.3	*"Bring thou this fiend of Scotland and myself; / Within my sword's length set him"*
Sadness	*Macduff*	4.3	*"But I must also feel it as a man: / I cannot but remember such things were, / That were most precious to me."*

Wrap-up

Emotions

Objective: Finding quotes that portray emotions

Activity

Macbeth is known for its intensity as a drama. For the duration of the play, characters are in a perpetual fight for survival. By murdering friends and enemies alike, Macbeth maintains an environment in which no character appears to be safe from harm.

The intense nature of *Macbeth* makes it a very emotional play. The **Emotion Chart** below contains a list of emotions depicted in the text. The location of each emotion is provided for you. Using the locations, find the source of each emotion. Identify the proper characters and quote them on the chart. The first entry has been completed for you.

Emotion Chart

Emotion	Source (character)	Act. Scene	Quote
Fear	Macbeth	1	"There is none but he / whose being I do fear"
Hatred		5.8	
Guilt		2.2	
Anxiety		3.4	
Love		1.5	
Wrath		4.3	
Sadness		4.3	

Wrap-up

Sequels

Objective: Writing creatively

Activity

Every day you see new sequels to books and movies, and quite frequently the sequels are not as entertaining as the originals. Some sequels are redundant because the elements that they share with the original episodes do not change. Sometimes, the original work is simply not a good basis for a sequel because it leaves no "loose ends" or unanswered questions to address in a sequel.

Macbeth contains loose ends that might provide a good foundation for a sequel. We have listed five examples for you. Using one or more for guidance, write a one-page summary of your sequel to *Macbeth*. Feel free to create new material to help your sequel, but make sure it is based on your ideas from *Macbeth*.

Example of loose ends:

1. Before dying, Banquo asks Fleance seek revenge; Fleance never does.
2. The witches go unpunished; their existence threatens future people.
3. Malcolm's unemotional reaction to his father's murder is "O, by whom?" He, like Macbeth, might also be evil.
4. It is not determined whether the witches truly have control over Macbeth's fate.
5. Malcolm becomes King, but, according to the prophecy, Fleance—Banquos son—should be King.

Example of possible sequel summary:

> After four uneventful years in Scotland, Malcolm still sits on the throne that he took from Macbeth. Fleance, now a young knight, reflects on his inability to act on his dead father's last wish for revenge. He also is bothered by a story that Banquo had revealed to him, about an accurate prophecy made by witches. He tries to dismiss the story as a tale, but never succeeds. Instead, Fleance slowly grows obsessed with the prophecy until Malcolm gives him a reason to act upon it.
>
> Macduff, now one of Malcolm's generals, has returned to Fife but pays close attention to Malcolm's questionable politics. Since the death of his family, he has only grown more distrustful to his colleagues.

Wrap-up

Sequels

Objective: Writing creatively

Activity

Every day you see new sequels to books and movies, and quite frequently the sequels are not as entertaining as the originals. Some sequels are redundant because the elements that they share with the original episodes do not change. Sometimes, the original work is simply not a good basis for a sequel because it leaves no "loose ends" or unanswered questions to address in a sequel.

Macbeth contains loose ends that might provide a good foundation for a sequel. We have listed five examples for you. Using one or more for guidance, write a one-page summary of your sequel to *Macbeth*. Feel free to create new material to help your sequel, but make sure it is based on your ideas from *Macbeth*.

Example of loose ends:

1. Before dying, Banquo asks Fleance seek revenge; Fleance never does.
2. The witches go unpunished; their existence threatens future people.
3. Malcolm's unemotional reaction to his father's murder is "O, by whom?" He, like Macbeth, might also be evil.
4. It is not determined whether the witches truly have control over Macbeth's fate.
5. Malcolm becomes King, but, according to the prophecy, Fleance—Banquos son—should be King.

Example of possible sequel summary:

> After four uneventful years in Scotland, Malcolm still sits on the throne that he took from Macbeth. Fleance, now a young knight, reflects on his inability to act on his dead father's last wish for revenge. He also is bothered by a story that Banquo had revealed to him, about an accurate prophecy made by witches. He tries to dismiss the story as a tale, but never succeeds. Instead, Fleance slowly grows obsessed with the prophecy until Malcolm gives him a reason to act upon it.
>
> Macduff, now one of Malcolm's generals, has returned to Fife but pays close attention to Malcolm's questionable politics. Since the death of his family, he has only grown more distrustful to his colleagues.

Wrap-up

Game Playing

Objective: Inventing a method to remember the events and characters of the play

Activity

One good way to remember facts is to answer questions about them. This helps to create associations between answers and questions, rather than simply answering questions. Using the entire play, write a set of "Jeopardy" questions that cover the categories on the board below.

Divide the class into two or four groups. Using the board below, each group should list at least fifteen answers to present to the rest of the class for questions. Include the act and scene in the answer if the material is quoted. Four answers are supplied for you.

Walking After Dark	Fatal Fortune	A Pair of Kings	Headhunting	Trouble Brewing
$200	MACDONWALD	$200	$200	$200
DONALBAIN	$400	$400	$400	HECATE
$800	$800	$800	SIWARD	$800
$1000	$1000	$1000	$1000	$1000

Wrap-up

Game Playing

Objective: Inventing a method to remember the events and characters of the play

Activity

One good way to remember facts is to answer questions about them. This helps to create associations between answers and questions, rather than simply answering questions. Using the entire play, write a set of "Jeopardy" questions that cover the categories on the board below.

Divide the class into two or four groups. Using the board below, each group should list at least fifteen answers to present to the rest of the class for questions. Include the act and scene in the answer if the material is quoted. Four answers are supplied for you.

Walking After Dark	Fatal Fortune	A Pair of Kings	Headhunting	Trouble Brewing
$200	MACDONWALD	$200	$200	$200
DONALBAIN	$400	$400	$400	HECATE
$800	$800	$800	SIWARD	$800
$1000	$1000	$1000	$1000	$1000

Sample Questions:

TROUBLE BREWING, $400: Who is the Queen of the Witches?

FATAL FATE, $200: Who does Macbeth kill in Act I?

WALKING AFTER DARK, $400: Who flees to Ireland after the murder of Duncan?

HEADHUNTING, $800: Who is the English general who attacks Macbeth?

Sample Questions:

TROUBLE BREWING, $400: Who is the Queen of the Witches?

FATAL FATE, $200: Who does Macbeth kill in Act I?

WALKING AFTER DARK, $400: Who flees to Ireland after the murder of Duncan?

HEADHUNTING, $800: Who is the English general who attacks Macbeth?

Wrap-up

Writing Headlines

Objective: Creating effective headlines

Activity

Many stories in magazines and tabloids use a one-line statement to briefly describe an article. Newspapers do not have this advantage; they must use concise, attention-grabbing headlines in order to spark the curiosity of potential readers. Unlike one-liners, headlines often only reveal the nature of articles and merely hint at what will follow. If the headline is enticing enough to capture the interest of the reader, the paper will sell.

The tragic nature of *Macbeth* provides for a wealth of potential headlines. Review the play and choose ten scenes that inspire the most exciting headlines. List your headlines and note the acts and scenes of their source.

Example:

WITCHES BREW TROUBLE	Act IV, Scene 1
DUNCAN MURDERED	*Act II, Scene 2*
BOY ESCAPES CUTTHROATS	*Act III, Scene 3*
SECRET MEETING OF GENERALS, WITCHES	*Act I, Scene 3*
MACBETH LOSING SUPPORT	*Act III, Scene 4*
MACDUFF FLEES COUNTRY	*Act IV, Scene 2*
WARNING MESSAGE FOR MOTHER, SON	*Act IV, Scene 2*
KING'S WIFE DEAD	*Act V, Scene 5*
DEAD GUARDS FRAMED	*Act II, Scene 3*
HEIRS FLEE KINGDOM	*Act II, Scene 4*

Wrap-up

Writing Headlines

Objective: Creating effective headlines

Activity

Many stories in magazines and tabloids use a one-line statement to briefly describe an article. Newspapers do not have this advantage; they must use concise, attention-grabbing headlines in order to spark the curiosity of potential readers. Unlike one-liners, headlines often only reveal the nature of articles and merely hint at what will follow. If the headline is enticing enough to capture the interest of the reader, the paper will sell.

The tragic nature of *Macbeth* provides for a wealth of potential headlines. Review the play and choose ten scenes that inspire the most exciting headlines. List your headlines and note the acts and scenes of their source.

Example:

WITCHES BREW TROUBLE   Act IV, Scene 1

Wrap-up

Characterization

Objective: Inferring character traits based on the action of the play

Activity

Divide the class into small groups. Each group should identify the traits that it thinks fit the character of Macbeth.

___1. shrewd	___11. impulsive	___21. loyal
___2. daring	___12. realist	___22. civilized
___3. dangerous	___13. imaginative	___23. composed
___4. resourceful	___14. content	___24. intelligent
___5. witty	___15. honorable	___25. rational
___6. humble	___16. generous	___26. gullible
___7. lonely	___17. brave	___27. funny
___8. angry	___18. simple	___28. stubborn
___9. quiet	___19. overbearing	___29. trusting
___10. greedy	___20. fair	___30. unpredictable

Of the traits identified for Macbeth, consider the following:

1. Which three or four of the traits do you infer from the character's comments or actions?

A.   B.   C.   D.

2. Which three or four of the traits do you identify because another character pointed it out?

A.   B.   C.   D.

3. Which three or four of the traits do you learn because the character tells you?

A.   B.   C.   D.

Of the three possible ways to learn character traits, which do you think is the most effective to help you understand Macbeth?

After you have decided which traits apply strongly to Macbeth, pick your top three and write a paragraph for each. The paragraphs should describe both how the trait is represented in the play and how you learn of it. Be specific in your analysis.

Wrap-up

Characterization

Objective: Inferring character traits based on the action of the play

Activity

Divide the class into small groups. Each group should identify the traits that it thinks fit the character of Macbeth.

___1.	shrewd	___11.	impulsive	___21.	loyal
___2.	daring	___12.	realist	___22.	civilized
___3.	dangerous	___13.	imaginative	___23.	composed
___4.	resourceful	___14.	content	___24.	intelligent
___5.	witty	___15.	honorable	___25.	rational
___6.	humble	___16.	generous	___26.	gullible
___7.	lonely	___17.	brave	___27.	funny
___8.	angry	___18.	simple	___28.	stubborn
___9.	quiet	___19.	overbearing	___29.	trusting
___10.	greedy	___20.	fair	___30.	unpredictable

Of the traits identified for Macbeth, consider the following:

1. Which three or four of the traits do you infer from the character's comments or actions?

A.   B.   C.   D.

2. Which three or four of the traits do you identify because another character pointed it out?

A.   B.   C.   D.

3. Which three or four of the traits do you learn because the character tells you?

A.   B.   C.   D.

Of the three possible ways to learn character traits, which do you think is the most effective to help you understand Macbeth?

After you have decided which traits apply strongly to Macbeth, pick your top three and write a paragraph for each. The paragraphs should describe both how the trait is represented in the play and how you learn of it. Be specific in your analysis.

Wrap-up

Crossword Puzzle

Objective: Identifying characters and setting using clues from the story

Activity

Complete the crossword puzzle using characters and places from *Macbeth*.

Wrap-up

Crossword Puzzle

Objective: Identifying characters and setting using clues from the story

Activity

Complete the crossword puzzle using characters and places from *Macbeth*.

Across

1 Duncan's kingdom
3 Takes the throne from Macbeth
7 Flees to Ireland after Duncan is murdered
9 ____ wood: Where Malcolm's army obtains camouflage
13 Macduff's land
14 The site of the final battle
15 Warns Lady Macduff
16 General killed by murderers
17 The leader of the witches

Down

2 Macbeth's first victim
4 Kills Macbeth
5 Flees when Banquo is murdered
6 English general who helps Macduff
8 Location of Macbeth's castle
10 Sends message to England to help Macduff
11 Nobleman who remains loyal to Macbeth
12 General who murders Duncan

Answer Key
Across
1. SCOTLAND
3. MALCOM
7. DONALBAIN
9. BIRNAM
13. FIFE
14. DUNSINANE
15. ROSS
16. BANQUO
17. HECATE

Down
2. DUNCAN
4. MACDUFF
5. FIFANCE
6. SIWARD
8. INVERNESS
10. LENNOX
11. SEYTON
12. MACBETH

Across

1 Duncan's kingdom
3 Takes the throne from Macbeth
7 Flees to Ireland after Duncan is murdered
9 ____ wood: Where Malcolm's army obtains camouflage
13 Macduff's land
14 The site of the final battle
15 Warns Lady Macduff
16 General killed by murderers
17 The leader of the witches

Down

2 Macbeth's first victim
4 Kills Macbeth
5 Flees when Banquo is murdered
6 English general who helps Macduff
8 Location of Macbeth's castle
10 Sends message to England to help Macduff
11 Nobleman who remains loyal to Macbeth
12 General who murders Duncan

Wrap-up

Creative Writing

Objective: Creating a review about the play

Activity

Find and read a few drama and movie reviews from the newspaper. Using them as guides, write a review of *Macbeth*. If you have seen a performance of *Macbeth*, use it to develop your review, but do not base what you write on acting, just the play itself.

Include at least one quote from the play, perhaps one that you feel has a great deal of impact. Remember to cite the act and scene.

Evaluate the play according to your opinion, but back up your reasoning with facts. The review should be at least three paragraphs long.

Wrap-up

Creative Writing

Objective: Creating a review about the play

Activity

Find and read a few drama and movie reviews from the newspaper. Using them as guides, write a review of *Macbeth*. If you have seen a performance of *Macbeth*, use it to develop your review, but do not base what you write on acting, just the play itself.

Include at least one quote from the play, perhaps one that you feel has a great deal of impact. Remember to cite the act and scene.

Evaluate the play according to your opinion, but back up your reasoning with facts. The review should be at least three paragraphs long.

Wrap-Up

Irony

Objective: Finding irony in the play

Activity

We see editorial cartoons in many magazines and nearly every newspaper. These cartoons are usually a humorous way of communicating the artist's message.

Many editorial cartoonists use irony as the subject matter for their cartoons. They identify ironic situations in economics or politics and draw cartoons that depict the irony. These cartoons appear on the opinion page because, though they are based on facts, the drawings are caricatures (exaggerations) of actual people or events, and they are frequently humorous and ironic. The drawings are ordinarily influenced by the artist's perspective of the situation.

You are now the political cartoonist for the Scotland Post, and, knowing about the *Macbeth* scandal, you must find some peculiar instance in the play to depict in a cartoon. Draw an editorial cartoon based on some event in *Macbeth*. Use any character(s) you wish. Supply a caption for your cartoon.

Wrap-Up

Irony

Objective: Finding irony in the play

Activity

We see editorial cartoons in many magazines and nearly every newspaper. These cartoons are usually a humorous way of communicating the artist's message.

Many editorial cartoonists use irony as the subject matter for their cartoons. They identify ironic situations in economics or politics and draw cartoons that depict the irony. These cartoons appear on the opinion page because, though they are based on facts, the drawings are caricatures (exaggerations) of actual people or events, and they are frequently humorous and ironic. The drawings are ordinarily influenced by the artist's perspective of the situation.

You are now the political cartoonist for the Scotland Post, and, knowing about the *Macbeth* scandal, you must find some peculiar instance in the play to depict in a cartoon. Draw an editorial cartoon based on some event in *Macbeth*. Use any character(s) you wish. Supply a caption for your cartoon.

Wrap-up

Quiz

Objective: Testing knowledge of the play

Activity

1. In what country does *Macbeth* take place?

Scotland

2. With whom does Duncan's army wage war in Act I?

Sweno, the King of Norway

3. Who is with Macbeth when the witches give him the prophecy?

Banquo

4. Where is Duncan murdered and what is he doing?

Duncan is murdered in his sleep at Macbeth's castle

5. How does Lady Macbeth keep the guards from stopping the murder?

She gets them drunk and drugs them.

6. How many murderers does Macbeth send to kill Banquo?

Three

7. What does Lady Macduff think about her husband in Act IV?

She thinks that he is a traitor because he fled the country.

8. What does Lady Macbeth do while she is sleepwalking?

She goes through the motions of washing her hands, and she talks about the murders.

9. Why is Macduff not born "of a woman"?

He was born by cesarean section—"from his mother's womb / Untimely ripp'd."

Wrap-up

Quiz

Objective: Testing knowledge of the play

Activity

1. In what country does *Macbeth* take place?

2. With whom does Duncan's army wage war in Act I?

3. Who is with Macbeth when the witches give him the prophecy?

4. Where is Duncan murdered and what is he doing?

5. How does Lady Macbeth keep the guards from stopping the murder?

6. How many murderers does Macbeth send to kill Banquo?

7. What does Lady Macduff think about her husband in Act IV?

8. What does Lady Macbeth do while she is sleepwalking?

10. Who is Hecate?

Queen of the witches, head of witchcraft

9. Why is Macduff not born "of a woman"?

10. Who is Hecate?

Wrap-up

Quotations

Objective: Identifying characters in the play

Activity

Below you will find two columns. The first is a list of quotes from *Macbeth*, and the second is a list of characters. Match up the quote with the person who said it.

_____	1.	"My wife kill'd too?"	A.	Macbeth
_____	2.	"And now about the cauldron sing, like elves and fairies in a ring"	B.	Duncan
_____	3.	"Why then, God's soldier be he! Had I as many sons . . . I would not wish them to a fairer death"	C.	Banquo
_____	4.	"You know not whether it was his wisdom or his fear."	D.	Lady Macduff
_____	5.	"Things have been strangely borne. The gracious Duncan was pitied of Macbeth: marry he was dead"	E.	Hecate
_____	6.	"What's he that was not born of a woman? Such a one am I to fear, or none."	F.	Lady Macbeth
_____	7.	"To Ireland, I; our separated fortune shall keep us both the safer"	G.	Macduff
_____	8.	"O, treachery! Fly, good Fleance, fly, fly, fly!"	H.	Ross
_____	9.	"The queen, my lord, is dead."	I.	Lennox
_____	10.	"Sirrah, your father's dead: And what will you do now?	J.	Siward
_____	11.	"I fear thy nature; It is too full o' the milk of human kindness to catch the nearest way"	K.	Seyton
_____	12.	"He was a gentleman on whom I built an absolute trust."	L.	Donalbain

Wrap-up

Quotations

Objective: Identifying characters in the play

Activity

Below you will find two columns. The first is a list of quotes from *Macbeth*, and the second is a list of characters. Match up the quote with the person who said it.

_____	1.	"My wife kill'd too?"	A.	Macbeth
_____	2.	"And now about the cauldron sing, like elves and fairies in a ring"	B.	Duncan
_____	3.	"Why then, God's soldier be he! Had I as many sons . . . I would not wish them to a fairer death"	C.	Banquo
_____	4.	"You know not whether it was his wisdom or his fear."	D.	Lady Macduff
_____	5.	"Things have been strangely borne. The gracious Duncan was pitied of Macbeth: marry he was dead"	E.	Hecate
_____	6.	"What's he that was not born of a woman? Such a one am I to fear, or none."	F.	Lady Macbeth
_____	7.	"To Ireland, I; our separated fortune shall keep us both the safer"	G.	Macduff
_____	8.	"O, treachery! Fly, good Fleance, fly, fly, fly!"	H.	Ross
_____	9.	"The queen, my lord, is dead."	I.	Lennox
_____	10.	"Sirrah, your father's dead: And what will you do now?	J.	Siward
_____	11.	"I fear thy nature; It is too full o' the milk of human kindness to catch the nearest way"	K.	Seyton
_____	12.	"He was a gentleman on whom I built an absolute trust."	L.	Donalbain

Answer Key

1.	G	7.	L
2.	E	8.	C
3.	J	9.	K
4.	H	10.	D
5.	I	11.	F
6.	A	12.	B

Macbeth

Activity Pack
Appendix

Small Group Learning

Small Group Learning is defined as two to five students working together for a common goal. For it to be successful, three basic elements must be present.

1. **SOCIAL SKILLS IN GROUP WORK:** Most students, unless they are taught the appropriate skills, do not participate as effectively as they might in small group work. Like any other skill, those needed for group work must be identified, practiced, and reinforced. To this end, we have included a Social Skills Behavior Checklist which we will ask you to use to rate your group. At this time, please read the related objectives listed below.

Social-Behavioral Objectives
1. Everyone is addressed by his or her first name.
2. Everyone speaks quietly in order not to disturb other groups.
3. No one ever uses put-downs or name calling.
4. Everyone is always physically and mentally part of the group. The following are prohibited and may result in the group's grade being lowered:
    A. Putting one's head down on the desk.
    B. Reading or working on unrelated items.
    C. Moving about the room or talking to members of other groups.
5. Everyone is encouraged to participate and does participate.
6. Everyone offers praise and encouragement.
7. Everyone recognizes that on some points of opinion two equally valid points of view can be supported.
8. Everyone also recognizes, however, that the worth of an idea (opinion) depends on the strength of the facts that support it.

Social-Intellectual Objectives

9. Ideas are discussed aloud.
10. Ideas are summarized.
11. Clarification is asked for and received.
12. Explanations are given until everyone understands.
13. Ideas, not people, are criticized.
14. Difficult ideas are paraphrased.
15. Multiple points of view are examined.
16. Work is organized within available time and available resources.
17. Questions are asked and answered satisfactorily.
18. Ideas are examined, elaborated on, and pulled together.
19. Reasons and rationale are asked for and provided.
20. Conclusions are challenged with new information.
21. Ideas are created in brainstorming.

2. **POSITIVE INTERDEPENDENCE:** Critical to successful *group work* is the realization on the part of the students "that we are all in this together; we either sink or swim as a group." In terms of this unit, it may mean that everyone in the group will share the group grade on the project, whether it is an "A" or an "F."

3. **INDIVIDUAL ACCOUNTABILITY:** The bottom line of any teaching method is, of course, how well the students have mastered the objectives being taught. Therefore, you must understand that the small group process, while it is more fun than other methods, is serious business. At the conclusion of this unit, a test may be used to evaluate how well each individual has mastered the objectives. As a consequence, the student who slacks off in the group or in his homework not only lets the group down, but also hurts him or herself.

Procedures For Small Group Work

As well as mastery of content and concepts, grades will be based on the demonstration of the following skills.

1. **Linguistic-Intellectual Skills** – These skills are fostered when students examine ideas from multiple points of view and critically probe for strengths and weaknesses.
2. **Group Social Skills** – Before anything else can be mastered, the small group must function effectively as a learning unit, which makes the mastery of these skills the first priority.

Linguistic-Intellectual Skills to be Demonstrated	Examples of these skills in action
Explaining	It seems to me… One way of looking at it… How does everyone feel about… The idea that…
Encouraging	What's your idea? I didn't think of that. Good idea! That helps. Good; go on with that thought.
Clarifying	Let's put it this way... Perhaps if we draw a chart... It may mean that.... How does this sound... Where does this lead us?
Elaborating	That's right and it also may include... Another instance of that is when... A point we might also include...
Qualifying	I agree with your premise, but... I see it leading somewhere else... That is one reason, but it may also... I agree with the examples, but I come to a different conclusion. Does that conclusion hold up in every instance?
Questioning	Why do you say that? What is the proof for that conclusion? Is that a valid generalization? How did you reach that point?
Disagreeing	It seems to me there could be a different reason. But looking at it from his point of view... We may be jumping to a conclusion without looking at all the facts. Here's another way of looking at it...

Small Group Evaluation Sheet

Social-Behavioral Skills in our group	**Poor**			**Good**	
1. Everyone is addressed by his or her first name.	1	2	3	4	5
2. Everyone speaks quietly. (If one group gets loud, other groups get louder to hear each other.)	1	2	3	4	5
3. No one ever uses put-downs or name calling.	1	2	3	4	5
4. Everyone is always physically and mentally part of the group.	1	2	3	4	5
5. Everyone is encouraged to and does participate.	1	2	3	4	5
6. Everyone offers praise and encouragement.	1	2	3	4	5
7. Everyone recognizes that on some opinions, two equally valid points of view can be supported.	1	2	3	4	5
8. Everyone also recognizes, however, that the worth of an idea (opinion) depends on the strength of the facts that support it.	1	2	3	4	5

Social-Intellectual Skills in our group					
9. Ideas are examined and discussed aloud.	1	2	3	4	5
10. Ideas are summarized.	1	2	3	4	5
11. Clarification is asked for and received.	1	2	3	4	5
12. Explanations are given until everyone understands.	1	2	3	4	5
13. Ideas, not people, are criticized.	1	2	3	4	5
14. Difficult ideas are paraphrased.	1	2	3	4	5
15. Multiple points of view are examined.	1	2	3	4	5
16. Work is organized within available time and available resources.	1	2	3	4	5
17. Questions are asked and answered satisfactorily.	1	2	3	4	5
18. Ideas are examined, elaborated on, and pulled together.	1	2	3	4	5
19. Reasons and rationales are asked for and provided.	1	2	3	4	5
20. Conclusions are challenged with new information.	1	2	3	4	5
21. Ideas are created in brainstorming.	1	2	3	4	5

Total Score _____

Student Roles In Group Discussions

1.   **Reader:** The reader's job is to read the questions aloud and to be sure everyone knows the meaning of unfamiliar words and understands the questions.

2.   **Recorder:** The recorder takes notes and is responsible for writing down the group's final answers.

3.   **Timer and Voice Monitor:** The timer and voice monitor is responsible for reminding individuals when they get too loud and for keeping track of the time. Because of a concern for finishing the project on time, the monitor will be the one to get the students back on task when they stray or get bogged down on one point.

4.   **Checker and Encourager:** This person's chief responsibility is to encourage all members to contribute, to compliment when appropriate, and to remind everyone of the necessity of avoiding name calling and/or put-downs.

Newspaper

News Article - This is an accurate and objective reporting of an event. News articles should include the "Five W's": What, When, Where, Who, and Why. A good newspaper writer usually can include all the necessary information in the first paragraph of the article. This is done so that readers can understand what the article is about simply by reading one paragraph and then deciding if they want to read further to get more detailed information.

The next paragraphs in the news article expand on the Five W's of the first paragraph.

Example:

Last night at 10 PM, a train from Philadelphia, PA to Pittsburgh slid off the tracks near Johnstown. No injuries were reported, but the train had been carrying flammable materials. A spokesperson for the Pennsylvania Railroad, Mr. Robert Graves, said that while there was no evidence of sabotage, "that possibility is being looked into by police." This is the second derailing on this route in two years.

The rest of the article would expand upon and give background and further information on the accident.

Editorial - This is a piece in which the writer gives opinions about an issue. A possible solution may be suggested. The requirements of the Five W's and absolute, unbiased accuracy are not adhered to as strictly as they are in a news article.

Example:

How many train wrecks will we have before the government steps in? Will it take a fatality before trains in our state are made safer? Should explosives, poisonous materials, and hazardous wastes continue to be shipped with only minor considerations to safety? This newspaper's opinion is a firm and resounding "No!" If the Federal Transportation Commission does not recognize its own failings and correct the problems, it will be our local politicians' job to re-route trains carrying potentially dangerous cargoes away from our communities.

Human-Interest Story - This type differs from the previous two because it has a different overall intent. As in a news article, the intent is to inform the reader of facts, but in the human-interest story, writers add the element of appealing to the readers' sympathies. Answering the Five W's is usually adhered to, but not as strictly as in the news article. Frequent topics of human-interest stories are animals, heroic deeds, strange occurrences of fate, money, etc.

Example:
Huddled among the broken railroad cars and destroyed contents of yesterday's train derailment near us, sat someone's lost puppy. Police found it early this morning after hearing whimpering from inside one of the cars. The poor dog's leg had been severed in the accident, and it was trapped by rubble. Had another hour elapsed, it probably would have died, says a local veterinarian, who treated the mixed-breed, black-and-white dog. According to the vet, Stumpy, as the dog is now called, has received more than twenty requests for adoption since his lucky rescue was accomplished.

Headline – This is a short heading over an article, which is set in large type, and which gives an indication of the subject of the article. Headlines are short and are designed to catch the readers' interest. All important words in the headline should be capitalized. Each article in a newspaper contains a headline. The wording of headlines is very important. If they say too much, readers may skip reading the article; if they are too vague, the subject may not interest the reader. Simple words such as *a, and, the* are frequently left out of headlines.

Examples:
Train Jumps Tracks; Second in Two Years

Two Train Wrecks Are Too Many

Injured Puppy Found in Train Debris

Directions for Interviews

Planning in Small Groups

First, discuss what you, as interviewer, want to know and the reasons you want to know it. Decide what you want to use as your specific questions.

Second, anticipate what the person being interviewed will answer. Use as many quotations from the text as possible. The answers should be consistent with things the character or narrative text says.

Finally, plan the interviewer's summary remark. Try to explain how the information in the questions/answers relates to the plot in general and thematic ideas of the novel.

Dramatization of Scenes in the Novel

Drama: Drama according to Aristotle is "imitated human action" presented through dialogue meant to instruct or entertain.

Dramatic Monologue: A person speaks to a silent audience, revealing an aspect of his or her character, expressing a viewpoint.

Comments: Often, sections of literary works seem to portray intense or captivating interaction, drama, between characters. While reading, visualize how the characters move in terms of their gestures and in relation to each other. See them touching each other or backing away. Hear the tones in their voices and the inflections, volume, and emphasis they use when they speak to each other. Imaginatively experience the feelings and meanings they are communicating to each other.

We do not expect that students will be above-average performers, and we do not feel they should be judged on "acting" as a major criterion in any dramatization. Students should be expected to capture the characters they portray and exhibit the truth of whatever the activity calls for. These types of activities are not intended to be polished Hollywood performances, nor the quality one would even see on a High School stage. That takes a class in drama or a group of talented performers who have a great deal of time to prepare. Our acting activities are designed only to reveal character or plot to the audience.

Terms and Definitions

Alliteration - the repetition of sounds at the beginning of words. **Example:** More Mischief and Merriment.

Characterization - the methods, incidents, speech, etc., an author uses to reveal the people in the book. Characterization is depicted by what the person says, what others say, and by his or her actions.

Foreshadowing - the use of hints or clues in a story to suggest what action is to come. Foreshadowing is frequently used to create interest and build suspense. **Example**: Two small and seemingly inconsequential car accidents predict and hint at the upcoming, important wreck in *The Great Gatsby*.

Inference - the act of drawing a conclusion that is not actually stated by the author. **Example**: In *The Pigman*, John and Lorraine are writing a "memorial epic" about Mr. Pignati. Therefore, the reader may logically assume that Mr. Pignati dies in the book.

Irony - a perception of inconsistency, sometimes humorous, in which the significance and understanding of a statement or event is changed by its context. **Example**: The firehouse burned down.
- *Dramatic Irony* - the audience or reader knows more about a character's situation than the character does and knows that the character's understanding is incorrect. **Example**: In *Medea*, Creon asks, "What atrocities could she commit in one day?" The reader, however, knows Medea will destroy her family and Creon's by day's end.
- *Structural Irony* – the use of a naïve hero, whose incorrect perceptions differ from the reader's correct ones. **Example**: Huck Finn.
- *Verbal Irony* - a discrepancy between what is said and what is really meant; sarcasm. **Example**: A large man whose nickname is "Tiny."

Metaphor - a comparison of two things that are basically dissimilar in which one is described in terms of the other. **Example**: The moon, a haunting lantern, shone through the clouds.

Setting - when and where the short story, play, or novel takes place. **Examples**: *Macbeth* takes place in the eleventh century in Scotland. *The Old Man and the Sea* has its main setting on the ocean outside Havana, Cuba, in an unspecified time in the middle-to-late 20th-century.

Simile - a comparison between two different things using either *like* or *as*. **Example**s: I am as hungry as a horse. The huge trees broke like twigs during the hurricane.

Symbol - an object, person, or place that has a meaning in itself and that also stands for something larger than itself, usually an idea or concept; some concrete thing which represents an abstraction. **Example**: The sea could be symbolic for "the unknown." Since the sea is something that is physical and can be seen by the reader, and also has elements that cannot be understood, it can be used symbolically to stand for the abstraction of "mystery," "obscurity," or "the unknown."

The Perfect Balance Between Cost and Quality for Classic Paperbacks

WITH ALL OF THE DIFFERENT EDITIONS of classics available, what makes *Prestwick House Literary Touchstone Classics*™ better?

Our editions were designed by former teachers with the needs of teachers and students in mind. Because we've struggled to stretch tight budgets and had to deal with the deficiencies of cheaply made paperbacks, we've produced high-quality trade editions at remarkably low prices. As a result, our editions have it all.

Value Pricing – With our extraordinary Educators' Discount, you get these books at **50% or more off the list price**.

Reading Pointers for Sharper Insights – Concise notes that encourage students to question and consider points of plot, theme, characterization, and style, etc.

Glossary and Vocabulary – An A-to-Z glossary makes sure that your students won't get lost in difficult allusions or archaic vocabulary and concepts.

Sturdy Bindings and High-Quality Paper – High-quality construction ensures these editions hold up to heavy, repeated use.

Strategies for Understanding Shakespeare – Each *Shakespeare Literary Touchstone Classic*™ contains line numbers, margin notes, and a guide to understanding Shakespeare's language, as well as key strategies for getting the most from the plays.

Special Introductory Discount for Educator's only – At Least 50% Off!
New titles are constantly being added, call or visit our website for current listing.

		Retail Price Intro.	Discount
200053	**Adventures of Huckleberry Finn** - *Twain* 🆃🆁🆃🆁	$4.99	$2.49
200473	**Adventures of Tom Sawyer, The** - *Twain* 🆃🆁🆃	$4.99	$2.49
202116	**Alice's Adventure in Wonderland** - *Carroll* 🆃🆁	$3.99	$1.99
202118	**Antigone** - *Sophocles* 🆃🆁🆃	$3.99	$1.99
200141	**Awakening, The** - *Chopin* 🆃🆁🆃🆁	$3.99	$1.99
202111	**Beowulf** - *Roberts (ed.)* 🆃	$3.99	$1.99
204866	**Best of Poe, The: The Tell-Tale Heart, The Raven, The Cask of Amontillado, and 30 Others** - *Poe*	$4.99	$2.49
200150	**Call of the Wild, The** - *London* 🆃🆁🆃	$3.99	$1.99
200348	**Canterbury Tales** - *Chaucer* 🆃	$3.99	$1.99
200179	**Christmas Carol, A** - *Dickens* 🆃🆁🆃	$3.99	$1.99
201198	**Crime and Punishment** - *Dostoyevsky* 🆃	$6.99	$3.49
200694	**Doll's House, A** - *Ibsen* 🆃🆁🆃	$3.99	$1.99
200190	**Dr. Jekyll and Mr. Hyde** - *Stevenson* 🆃🆁🆃	$3.99	$1.99

202113	**Dracula** - *Stoker* 🆃🆁	$5.99	$2.99
200166	**Ethan Frome** - *Wharton* 🆃🆁🆃	$3.99	$1.99
200054	**Frankenstein** - *Shelley* 🆃🆁🆃🆁	$4.99	$1.99
202112	**Great Expectations** - *Dickens* 🆃🆁🆃🆁	$5.99	$2.99
202108	**Gulliver's Travels** - *Swift* 🆃	$4.99	$2.49
200091	**Hamlet** - *Shakespeare* 🆃🆁🆃🆁	$3.99	$1.99
200074	**Heart of Darkness** - *Conrad* 🆃🆁🆃	$3.99	$1.99
202117	**Hound of the Baskervilles, The** - *Doyle* 🆃🆁🆃	$3.99	$1.99
200147	**Importance of Being Earnest, The** - *Wilde* 🆃🆁🆃	$3.99	$1.99
301414	**Invisible Man, The** - *Wells* 🆃🆁	$3.99	$1.99
202115	**Jane Eyre** - *Brontë* 🆃🆁	$6.99	$3.49
200146	**Julius Caesar** - *Shakespeare* 🆃🆁🆃	$3.99	$1.99
201817	**Jungle, The** - *Sinclair* 🆃🆁🆃	$5.99	$2.99
200125	**Macbeth** - *Shakespeare* 🆃🆁🆃🆁	$3.99	$1.99
204864	**Medea** - *Euripides* 🆃	$3.99	$1.99
200133	**Metamorphosis, The** - *Kafka* 🆃🆁	$3.99	$1.99
200081	**Midsummer Night's Dream, A** - *Shakespeare* 🆃🆁🆃	$3.99	$1.99
202123	**Much Ado About Nothing** - *Shakespeare* 🆃🆁🆃	$3.99	$1.99
301391	**My Antonia** - *Cather* 🆃🆁	$3.99	$1.99
200079	**Narrative of the Life of Frederick Douglass** - *Douglass* 🆃🆁🆃	$3.99	$1.99
301269	**Odyssey, The** - *Butler (trans.)* 🆃🆁🆃	$4.99	$2.49
200564	**Oedipus Rex** - *Sophocles* 🆃	$3.99	$1.99
200095	**Othello** - *Shakespeare* 🆃🆁🆃🆁	$3.99	$1.99
202121	**Picture of Dorian Gray, The** - *Wilde* 🆃🆁	$4.99	$2.49
200368	**Pride and Prejudice** - *Austen* 🆃🆁🆃	$4.99	$2.49
202114	**Prince, The** - *Machavelli* 🆃	$3.99	$1.99
200791	**Pygmalion** - *Shaw* 🆃	$3.99	$1.99
200102	**Red Badge of Courage, The** - *Crane* 🆃🆁🆃	$3.99	$1.99
200193	**Romeo and Juliet** - *Shakespeare* 🆃🆁🆃	$3.99	$0.99
200132	**Scarlet Letter, The** - *Hawthorne* 🆃🆃🆁	$4.99	$2.49
202119	**Siddhartha** - *Hesse* 🆃🆁🆃	$3.99	$1.99
204863	**Silas Marner** - *Eliot* 🆃🆁🆃	$3.99	$1.99
200251	**Tale of Two Cities, A** - *Dickens* 🆃🆁	$5.99	$2.99
200231	**Taming of the Shrew, The** - *Shakespeare* 🆃🆁🆃	$3.99	$1.99
204865	**Time Machine, The** - *Wells* 🆃🆁🆃	$3.99	$1.99
202120	**Treasure Island** - *Stevenson* 🆃🆁	$4.99	$2.49
301420	**War of the Worlds** - *Wells* 🆃🆁	$3.99	$1.99
202122	**Wuthering Heights** - *Brontë* 🆃🆃	$5.99	$2.99

🆃 Teaching Units 🆁 Response Journals 🆃 Activity Pack 🆁 AP Teaching Units

PH PRESTWICK HOUSE, INC.
"Everything for the English Classroom!"

P.O. Box 658 • Clayton, DE 19938 • (800) 932-4593 • (888) 718-9333 • www.prestwickhouse.com

PRESTWICK HOUSE, INC.

Order Form

Call 1-800-932-4593 Fax 1-888-718-9333

Prestwick House, Inc.
P.O. Box 658
Clayton, DE 19938

Bill To: ■Home ■School

School:

Name:

Address:

City, State, Zip:

Phone: Email:

Ship To: ■Home ■School

School:

Name:

Address:

City, State, Zip:

Phone: Email:

ITEM NO	TITLE	QUANTITY	X	PRICE	=	TOTAL

Subtotal	$
Shipping 12% S&H ($6.00 minimum)	$
Total	$

Method of Payment (Choose one)

❏ **Check or Money Order Enclosed**

❏ Visa ❏ MasterCard ❏ Discover Card ❏ American Express

❏ **Purchase Order Enclosed**
We accept purchase orders and authorized orders charged to institutions. Personal orders not on a credit card must be accompanied by a check.

Signature

Telephone #   Exp. Date

Credit Card #

Shipping & Handling
For orders of $50.00 or less, please add $6.00 for shipping and handling charges. For orders from $50.01 to $799.99 add 12% For orders of $800.00 and more, add 10%

Delivery Service
Most orders are shipped FedEx and you can expect delivery within 7-10 working days. Items in stock are usually shipped within one working day of receiving your order.

Expedited Delivery
for expedited delivery ask about the following options:
• Overnight Air
• 2nd day air
• 3 Day Select

Because charges for air delivery are based on weight and distance, heavy packages can be expensive to ship air freight. Typographic and photographic errors are subject to revision. Prestwick House is the sole source of all proprietary materials listed in this catalogue. Please be sure to include a street address. FedEx ground/UPS will not deliver to a P.O. Box.